■SCHOLASTIC

CW00394857

NO FUSS

YEAR 3
PHOTOCOPIABLES

All you need to teach 11 curriculum subjects!

AGES 7-8

- Levelled and linked to the curriculum

- Stand-alone photocopiable activities

- Ideal for mixed-age classes

Paul Noble and Jean Noble

AUTHORS

Paul Noble and Jean Noble

DEVELOPMENT EDITOR

Kate Pedlar

PROJECT EDITOR

Fabia Lewis

DESIGNERS

Q2a Media

COVER DESIGN

Anna Oliwa

ILLUSTRATOR

Ann Kronheimer

Text © 2008, Paul Noble and Jean Noble
© 2008, Scholastic Ltd

Published by Scholastic Ltd
Villiers House
Clarendon Avenue
Leamington Spa
Warwickshire
CV32 5PR
www.scholastic.co.uk

Designed using Adobe InDesign
Printed by Bell & Bain Ltd, Glasgow

1 2 3 4 5 6 7 8 9   8 9 0 1 2 3 4 5 6 7

British Library Cataloguing-in-Publication Data
A catalogue record for this book is available from the
British Library.

ISBN 978-1407-10095-1

The rights of Paul Noble and Jean Noble to be identified
as the authors of this work have been asserted by them in
accordance with the Copyright, Designs and Patents Act
1988.

Due to the nature of the web, the publisher cannot
guarantee the content or links of any of the websites
referred to. It is the responsibility of the reader to assess
the suitability of websites and check that links are still live.

Every effort has been made to trace copyright holders
for the works reproduced in this book, and the publishers
apologise for any inadvertent omissions.

www.scholastic.co.uk

CONTENTS

CONTENTS

SCHOLASTIC
www.scholastic.co.uk

INTRODUCTION

This is a straightforward compilation of stand-alone photocopiable activities for children in Year 3.

Ranging across the curriculum as they do, the activities within this book provide material for the National Curriculum subjects (except PE) plus Religious Education, PSHE and Citizenship. Although understandably not comprehensive in its National Curriculum coverage, this volume brings together a selection of previously published Scholastic photocopiables that have all been successfully tried and tested. You can use them with confidence and No Fuss.

At the heart of the book are the activity sheets presented with a concise and factual **curriculum grid**, which, in note form, cross-references the content of the sheets to: the National Curriculum, the Primary Framework, QCA schemes of work and where appropriate, to the Curriculum for Excellence (Scotland). Objectives for each activity sheet are stated and brief guidance notes are given to its use.

Within the curriculum grid, links are made to National Curriculum Attainment Targets and attainment levels as well as to the non-statutory Attainment Targets for RE.

Before you use any worksheet it is recommended that you refer to the curriculum grid so that you are clear about the objectives and are aware of any special demands made by the activity.

Year 3 children go through a phase of physical change while moving from an infant class to a junior one. For some, this also means a change of school. There is still a cultural difference between 'junior' and 'infant' schooling and although the National Curriculum aims to make this transition seamless, it is still a year of change. Many teachers notice how different a Year 3 class is during January from what it was in September when the year began.

Children face the whole range of curriculum subjects, as before, but the content of subjects is more precisely defined. This makes the construction of supportive material such as these worksheets a little more problematic. Choices can be made and it is obvious that not everyone will choose to do the same thing. However, learning, particularly within the Primary Framework is laid down in detail, and elsewhere we have been able to lean heavily upon the schemes of work from the QCA.

You will find this book particularly helpful when you are limited by time or have to meet the needs of voracious learners. Supply teachers and others 'caught on the hop' will also be able to rely on this material to help them to cope with demanding days.

You will hardly need reminding that although these worksheets will support your teaching, they cannot do it for you. A whole school full of over-heated photocopiers will not make children learn; it is for you to capture their interest and to provide the intellectual stimulus and practical experience that needs to accompany learning.

Page	Activity	Objectives	Teachers' notes	NC, QCA & Primary Framework	Curriculum for Excellence (Scotland)	AT links and levels
15	Words in words	To be able to recognise short words within long words.	Demonstrate some examples on the whiteboard first and make it clear that you are not looking for anagrams.	Literacy Strand 5 – Word recognition	LIT 002A/LW – Enjoyment and choice (reading) LIT 010N/X – Tools for reading and writing	AT2 Level 1 AT3 Level 1
16	Compounds in the playground	To be able to identify and spell some compound words.	Make sure the children can recognise compound words such as 'playground'. They may find more words than there are blanks.	Literacy Strand 5 – Word recognition	LIT 002A/LW – Enjoyment and choice (reading) LIT 010N/X – Tools for reading and writing	AT3 Level 2
17	New words for old	To recognise and construct compound words.	The new words should construct a word picture of the object. Make the exercise a bit of fun.	Literacy Strand 5 – Word recognition	LIT 002A/LW – Enjoyment and choice (reading) LIT 010N/X – Tools for reading/writing	AT2 Level 2 AT3 Level 2
18	The silence in lambs	To know that some words contain silent letters.	Encourage the use of dictionaries. Children do, of course, need to know that silent letters exist in some words.	Literacy Strand 6 – Word structure and spelling	LIT 002A/LW – Enjoyment and choice (reading) LIT 010N/X – Tools for reading	AT2 Level 2 AT3 Level 2
19	Word blender	To use knowledge of phonemes and segment words to improve accuracy in spelling.	Legitimate words are stressed here although children should learn to recognise non-words.	Literacy Strand 6 – Word structure and spelling	LIT 002A/LW – Enjoyment and choice (reading) LIT 010N/X – Tools for reading	AT2 Level 2 AT3 Level 2
20	Put back the missing 'le'	To investigate and spell words ending in 'le'.	Sever 'le' to demonstrate what the exercise is about: *We are going to do a simp exercise and should not get into a mudd.*	Literacy Strand 6 – Word structure and spelling	LIT 002A/LW – Enjoyment and choice (reading) LIT 010N/X – Tools for reading	AT2 Level 2 AT3 Level 2
21	'Re' chart	To spell words with the prefix 're' and to understand how its use modifies meaning.	The children can include a word of their own to at the bottom of the sheet. *How has the meaning of the old word changed?*	Literacy Strand 6 – Word structure and spelling	LIT 002A/LW – Enjoyment and choice (reading) LIT 112N – Tools for reading	AT2 Level 2 AT3 Level 2
22	'Un' web	To spell words with the prefix 'un' and to understand how its use modifies meaning.	As with the previous sheet the children can insert an example of their own. Follow up the exercise with discussion and analysis.	Literacy Strand 6 – Word structure and spelling	LIT 002A/LW – Enjoyment and choice (reading) LIT 112N – Tools for reading	AT2 Level 2 AT3 Level 2
23	Where's 'y'?	To recognise the suffix 'y' and to recognise how its use modifies meaning and spelling.	Demonstrate using an example. Pay particular attention to how the spelling of the root word can be changed when the suffix is added: eg bone/bony; mud/muddy. Write out the full sentences.	Literacy Strand 6 – Word structure and spelling	LIT 002A/LW – Enjoyment and choice (reading) LIT 112N – Tools for reading	AT2 Level 2 AT3 Level 2
24	Weather forecast	To recognise and spell words containing common suffixes and understand how the use of a suffix modifies meaning.	This is a reversal of the task on the previous sheet: now children are asked to identify the root word.	Literacy Strand 6 – Word structure and spelling	LIT 002A/LW – Enjoyment and choice (reading) LIT 112N – Tools for reading	AT2 Level 2 AT3 Level 2
25	Suffix chains	To recognise and spell words containing common suffixes and understand how the use of a suffix modifies meaning.	Examine an example of a suffix chain and talk about how meaning is changed. There is a blank so that children can choose their own root word and two chain words.	Literacy Strand 6 – Word structure and spelling	LIT 002A/LW – Enjoyment and choice (reading) LIT 112N – Tools for reading	AT2 Level 2 AT3 Level 2
26	Fixing suffixes	To understand how words are modified when the suffixes 'er' and 'est' are added.	You might start with the illustrations: *What do they show? What do you think might go into the blanks?*	Literacy Strand 6 – Word structure and spelling	LIT 002A/LW – Enjoyment and choice (reading) LIT 112N – Tools for reading	AT2 Level 2 AT3 Level 2
27	Step on the verb	To be able to identify verbs correctly.	Can the pirate reach the treasure without stepping on a crocodile (or flying like Peter Pan)? As the pirate can only tread on verbs children must first understand what a verb is.	Literacy Strand 11 – Sentence structure and punctuation	LIT 121Y – Tools for writing	AT2 Level 2 AT3 Level 2
28	Where's the verb?	To be able to construct sentences that include verbs. To notice how essential verbs are to the making of coherent meaning.	Have fun with examples, such as: 'I ___ my dinner at lunchtime'. The examples on the sheet expect answers that generate traditional nursery rhyme lines but you could extend this by thinking of alternative verbs. For example, 'Mary ate a little lamb'.	Literacy Strand 11 – Sentence structure and punctuation	LIT 122Z – Tools for writing	AT2 Level 2 AT3 Level 2
29	'ing' wheel	To know how the spellings of some verbs are modified when the prefix 'ing' is added.	Do examples with the children first, such as work/working and hope/hoping so that they understand that they are looking for a possible spelling change in the root part of the word.	Literacy Strand 11 – Sentence structure and punctuation	LIT 002A/LW – Enjoyment and choice (reading) LIT 112N – Tools for reading	AT2 Level 2 AT3 Level 2
30	Computer error	To recognise incorrect use of verb tenses. To learn a range of verbs used to introduce and conclude dialogue.	Read the story with dramatic emphasis. Quiz the children: Do they think the girl would really have said 'Help'? They may choose to write over the verb, rewrite or even retype the entire story.	Literacy Strand 11 – Sentence structure and punctuation	LIT 122Z – Tools for writing	AT3 Level 3

NO FUSS PHOTOCOPIABLE

Page	Activity	Objectives	Teachers' notes	NC, QCA & Primary Framework	Curriculum for Excellence (Scotland)	AT links and levels
31	Synonym search	To understand the term 'synonym'. To generate synonyms for high frequency words.	'Nice' is a tricky word to generate synonyms for as it is used for so many (often inappropriate) occasions and not always for its 'fine' meaning. You can give greater focus by displaying a sentence with the word 'nice' embedded for the children to reflect upon: 'That was nice singing', for example. The hidden words are: enjoyable, pretty, lovely, fine, superb, delightful, good, splendid, polite.	Literacy Strand 6 – Word structure and spelling	LIT 101A/LVV – Enjoyment and choice (reading) LIT 010N/X – Tools for reading	AT2 Level 3
32	Lists of opposites	To explore antonyms.	This is a straightforward sheet but teaching about antonyms needs to precede its use.	Literacy Strand 6 – Word structure and spelling	LIT 101A/LVV – Enjoyment and choice (reading) LIT 010N/X – Tools for reading LIT 120X – Tools for writing	AT3 Level 2/3
33	DIY dictionary	To be able to create dictionary definitions of words.	Play dictionary games: I have just arrived from Mars. I don't know what an orange is. What does the dictionary tell me? When the children are clear what a definition is introduce the sheet. Encourage brevity. Who can write the shortest good definition?	Literacy Strand 7 – Understanding and interpreting texts	LIT121Y – Tools for writing	AT3 Level 2/3
34	The long and short of it	To know how to use the apostrophe to spell shortened forms of words.	Ensure that the children understand what contractions are and let them search for these in their reading books. Talk about what they discover. Watch out for the possessive apostrophe and make sure that the children don't confuse the two.	Literacy Strand 6 – Word structure and spelling	LIT 120X – Tools for writing	AT3 Level 2/3
35	Making plurals	To investigate the rules for generating plurals.	Point out that the nouns have been grouped according to how their plurals are formed. The challenge here is for the children to be able to extract the general rule from the specific examples.	Literacy Strand 6 – Word structure and spelling	LIT 120X – Tools for writing	AT3 Level 2/3
36	Odd plurals	To recognise that some plurals do not comply with common rules.	Be selective about when you choose to use this sheet. It is important that children are secure in their knowledge of the 'law abiding' plurals before moving on to the 'criminal' cases.	Literacy Strand 6 – Word structure and spelling	LIT 120X – Tools for writing	AT3 Level 2/3
37	Ten to Tooting	To learn how to use alliteration to create sound effects when writing poetry.	Demonstrate alliterative sounds (you may not want to use the term at this stage). Work with the whole class and see who can come up with the most outrageous suggestions for the next lines. Encourage children to sound out the lines to make sure that they have continued the alliterative effect.	Literacy Strand 9 – Creating and shaping texts	LIT 010N/X – Tools for writing LIT 125AC – Organising and using information	AT3 Level 2
38	Confusing cuttings (1)	To be able to distinguish between fiction and non-fiction.	Teaching about the difference should precede this sheet. Discuss what clues in the writing lead them to make their decisions.	Literacy Strand 10 – Text structure and organisation	LIT 118U; LIT 116S – Understanding, analysing and evaluating (reading)	AT2 Level 3
39	Confusing cuttings (2)	To be able to distinguish between fiction and non-fiction.	This sheet can be used in the same way as the previous one.	Literacy Strand 10 – Text structure and organisation	LIT 118U; LIT 116S – Understanding, analysing and evaluating (reading)	AT2 Level 3
40	Off-the-peg rhymes	To be able to write a simple rhyming poem.	Draw attention to the items on the washing line wherein lie the answers. You may, of course, remove two of these prop for some children.	Literacy Strand 9 – Creating and shaping texts	LIT 010N/X – Tools for writing LIT 125AC – Organising and using information	AT2 Level 2 AT3 Level 2
41	Crash chaos	To recount events in the style of a newspaper report.	A few real examples of newspaper headlines should be shown to the class. Talk about the function of the headline and how the report should follow its lead. Examine the picture for text to put in the report: work from the pictorial evidence.	Literacy Strand 9 – Creating and shaping texts	LIT 121Y – Tools for writing	AT3 Level 3
42	Keeping count	To practise counting on and backwards in steps of 1, 10, or 100 from any two- or three-digit number.	Check understanding of the terms 'on' and 'back' first. Discuss the patterns that occur as the sheet is coloured in. Squares must be lightly coloured using pencils: do not obscure the figures.	Maths Strand – Counting and understanding number	MNU 001B – Number processes MNU 103C – Addition, subtraction, multiplication and division	AT2 Level 2

Page	Activity	Objectives	Teachers' notes	NC, QCA & Primary Framework	Curriculum for Excellence (Scotland)	AT links and levels
43	Big steps	To practise counting on and back in steps of 10 or 100 from any number.	Once again an understanding of 'on' and 'back' is necessary. This is an extension of the activity on the previous sheet.	Maths Strand – Counting and understanding number	MNU 001B – Number processes MNU 103C – Addition, subtraction, multiplication and division	AT2 Level 2/3
44	The missing thinks	To practise counting on or back in steps of any size.	Practise sequences similar to those on the sheet as mental exercises first: 1, 3, 5, 7… and so on. Make sure that children understand that they have to explain the rules for generating a number in the sequence.	Maths Strand – Counting and understanding number	MNU 001B – Number processes MNU 103C – Addition, subtraction, multiplication and division	AT2 Level 2
45	Multiples	To be able to derive and recall familiar multiples.	Check that the term 'multiple' is understood with a little oral practice. Point out that the rhyme is made up of multiples if they don't spot it themselves.	Maths Strand – Knowing and using number facts	MNU 103C – Addition, subtraction, multiplication and division	AT2 Level 2
46	Boxed in	To know what each digit of a number represents and to partition a number into multiples of 100, 10 and 1.	There are a number of ways that you may demonstrate how place value works using apparatus. It is not a concept that is always easily grasped and will need much reinforcement.	Maths Strand – Counting and understanding number	MNU 001B – Number processes MNU 102B – Addition, subtraction, multiplication and division	AT2 Level 3
47	Piggy in the middle	To compare numbers and to give a number that is halfway between them.	Work through some similar examples first: *What is halfway between 10 and 12?* and so on.	Maths Strand – Counting and understanding number	MNU 103C – Addition, subtraction, multiplication and division	AT2 Level 2/3
48	One hundred more or less	To be able to count on and back in steps of 100 from any number.	Completion of the boxes should not pose too many problems if children have begun to grasp the concept of place value.	Maths Strand – Counting and understanding number	MNU 001B – Number processes MNU 103C – Addition, subtraction, multiplication and division	AT2 Level 2/3
49	More or less: problems	To be able to choose and carry out calculations to solve problems.	Really these are straightforward 'sums', but children have to read and understand the problem in order to get to the point where arithmetic can take over.	Maths Strands – Using and applying mathematics; Calculating	MNU 103C – Addition, subtraction, multiplication and division	AT2 Level 2/3
50	Keeping order	To be able to read, write and order whole numbers.	Awareness of place value will lead the children to realise that the highest 'placed' digit – not the units – determines the outcome.	Maths Strand – Counting and understanding number	MNU 102B – Number processes MNU 006M – Measurement	AT2 Level 2/3
51	To the nearest 10	To be able to round numbers to the nearest 10.	The vocabulary and concept of rounding needs to be taught. Demonstrate rounding up for numbers that fall halfway.	Maths Strand – Counting and understanding number	MNU 101A – Estimation and rounding	AT2 Level 2/3
52	To the nearest 100	To be able to round numbers to the nearest 100.	This is the same as the previous sheet but children are required to use larger numbers.	Maths Strand – Counting and understanding number	MNU 101A – Estimation and rounding	AT2 Level 2/3
53	Shady fractions	To know how to read fractions and identify fractions of shapes.	There is no right way to colour the squares and the children should explore this for themselves. Concrete experience is an essential prerequisite here.	Maths Strand – Counting and understanding number	MNU 104H – Fractions, decimals and percentages	AT2 Level 3
54	Working out fractions	To know how to read and write fractions and identify fractions of shapes. To be able to find unit fractions of numbers and shapes.	Children only have to estimate the fractions shown in the last task, not measure them accurately.	Maths Strands – Counting and understanding number; Calculating	MNU 104H – Fractions, decimals and percentages	AT2 Level 3
55	Sum totals	To identify number pairs that total 100. To practise adding two-digit numbers.	Work through some examples together first. The answer to the last problem is: 189; 216; 244; 128; 156; 209; 270; 217; 182 and 163.	Maths Strands – Knowing and using number facts; Calculating	MTH 117R – Expressions and equations MTH 118R – Expressions and equations	AT2 Level 2
56	Meaty sums	To learn how to use addition to solve problems involving money.	Introduce the idea of a shopping receipt: use coins or toy money if necessary. (The answers to the questions on the sheet depend on the choice of items.)	Maths Strands – Using and applying mathematics; Calculating	MNU 103C – Addition, subtraction, multiplication and division MNU 107K – Money	AT1 Level 2 AT2 Level 2
57	Double trouble	To learn how to derive addition facts for pairs of the same number.	Making explicit how the answers are achieved is important and should be done orally to an adult. Explanation: *if you know that 20 + 20 = 40 and that 1 + 1 = 2 then 19 + 19 is 40 – 2 = 38.*	Maths Strand – Knowing and using number facts	MNU 103C – Addition, subtraction, multiplication and division	AT2 Level 2/3

Page	Activity	Objectives	Teachers' notes	NC, QCA & Primary Framework	Curriculum for Excellence (Scotland)	AT links and levels
58	Hundreds that make a thousand	To learn to add and subtract mentally numbers that total 1000.	The arithmetic is one aspect of this sheet but the children must also be able to read carefully and understand the problems.	Maths Strands – Knowing and using number facts; Calculating	MNU 103C – Addition, subtraction, multiplication and division	AT1 Level 2 AT2 Level 2/3
59	Add it up! Write it down!	To develop written methods for addition.	Demonstrate how the working out might be written down, particularly the use of brackets. Logical setting down of the thought process is just as important as the correct answer so look for sound reasoning.	Maths Strands – Using and applying mathematics; Calculating	MNU 103C – Addition, subtraction, multiplication and division	AT2 Level 2/3
60	Zigzags	To develop written methods for subtraction.	This is a companion to the previous sheet and a similar approach should be used. More confident learners can begin to record their working out vertically, lining up the units and tens.	Maths Strands – Using and applying mathematics; Calculating	MNU 103C – Addition, subtraction, multiplication and division	AT2 Level 2/3
61	Multiplying problems	To learn how to represent problems as multiplication. To be able to use written methods to multiply one- and two-digit numbers.	Explain to children what they are looking for and how to set down the calculation, for example: 4 × 6 = 24.	Maths Strands – Using and applying mathematics; Calculating	MNU 103C – Addition, subtraction, multiplication and division	AT1 Level 2 AT2 Level 2/3
62	Leftovers	To learn how to give a whole number and remainder when one number is divided by another.	Talk through some division examples similar to those on the sheet, working out answers mentally. Introduce the word 'remainder' and encourage children to jot down their thought process on the sheet.	Maths Strand – Using and applying mathematics; Calculating	MNU 103C – Addition, subtraction, multiplication and division	AT1 Level 2 AT2 Level 3
63	Puzzle page	To be able to solve problems using additions and multiplication facts.	Confirm that the children know and understand the terms 'sum' and 'product'. Answers are: **Part 2** (2, 2), (6, 3), (10, 6), (4, 3), (10, 10); **Part 3** 1 + 6 + 2, 2 + 4 + 3 and 3 + 5 + 1 (going clockwise around the triangle).	Maths Strand – Knowing and using number facts	MNU 103C; MNU 203C – Addition, subtraction, multiplication and division	AT2 Level 3
64	Taking readings	To practise reading and interpreting scales.	Use practical equipment and make sure that children are familiar with the measures involved. Note the option to record time in several different ways, for example, '10.25' or '25 past 10'.	Maths Strand – Measuring	MNU 112M – Measurement.	AT3 Level 2/3
65	Shaping up	To describe and classify common 2D shapes according to their properties.	Each description is exclusive.	Maths Strand – Understanding shape	MTH 119S – Properties of 2D shapes and 3D objects	AT3 Level 2
66	Lines of symmetry	To recognise lines of symmetry in shapes.	Teaching about symmetry must precede the use of this sheet. Can children spot shapes that have more than one line of symmetry (for example, the Union Jack)?	Maths Strand – Understanding shape	MTH 119S – Properties of 2D shapes and 3D objects MTH 123V – Angle, symmetry and transformation	AT3 Level 3
67	Where are they?	To be able to describe positions on a grid.	Play Noughts and Crosses, Battleships or any game that will get children used to the notion of locating positions on a grid. Teach the 'x first, y second' convention (we go into the house first before we go up the stairs).	Maths Strand – Understanding shape	MTH 122U – Angle, symmetry and transformation	AT3 Level 1
68	Right angle test	To learn how to use a rough template to identify right angles.	The tearing and folding is difficult so work with the children. Demonstrate by using a piece of newspaper, torn with no straight edges. Show how the right angle made can be tested against right angles in the room (eg the corner of a window pane).	Maths Strand – Understanding shape	MTH 226T – Angle, symmetry and transformation	AT3 Level 2/3
69	A varied diet	To understand that an adequate and healthy diet is needed for growth and activity.	The sheet shows simplified concepts to be built on later. Make sure that the term 'diet' is understood and not just in the narrow sense of 'reduced food intake for the purpose of losing weight'.	Science NC: Sc2 Humans and other animals QCA: Unit 3A Teeth and eating	SCN 005H – Energy in food	AT1 Level 2 AT2 Level 2/3
70	The truth about teeth	To learn about the different types of teeth and their functions.	Hopefully you will be able to show models of the teeth described on the sheet. Answers are: **1.** milk **3.** decay **5.** molars **6.** gums (across); **2.** incisors **4.** canines (down).	Science NC: Sc2 Humans and other animals QCA: Unit 3A Teeth and eating	SCN 112M – Keeping my body healthy	AT1 Level 2 AT2 Level 2/3

Page	Activity	Objectives	Teachers' notes	NC, QCA & Primary Framework	Curriculum for Excellence (Scotland)	AT links and levels
71	Tooth decay	To understand that some foods damage the health of teeth by causing decay.	With reference to a set of teeth explain the diagram. Explanations should include decay, bad eating habits, poor hygiene and the role of bacteria. Be positive with reference to dentistry: it is about prevention as much as treatment and repair.	Science NC: Sc2 Humans and other animals QCA: Unit 3A Teeth and eating	SCN 112M – Keeping my body healthy	AT2 Level 2/3
72	Tooth damage	To identify particular foods as damaging to teeth and others as less damaging.	This sheet should be used to build on previous work. Note the terms 'damaging' and 'less damaging'. Encourage children to add more foods of their own to the sets.	Science NC: Sc2 Humans and other animals QCA: Unit 3A Teeth and eating	SCN 112M – Keeping my body healthy	AT2 Level 2/3
73	Celery science	To ask questions about the growth of plants.	Children are recording their observations of a small experiment. You will need the equipment as described on the sheet. The diagrams should be a record of the process – a record of change.	Science NC: Sc2 Green plants QCA: Unit 3B Helping plants grow well	SCN 103B – Biodiversity	AT1 Level 2 AT2 Level 2
74	Eating the countryside	To recognise that plants can provide food for us and that some plants are grown for that purpose.	The edible plants (grown in this country) are wheat, beans, lettuce/cabbage, apples, pears, strawberries. In their own list children may include foods not grown in this country such as bananas.	Science NC: Sc2 Humans and other animals QCA: Unit 3A Teeth and eating	SCN 005H – Energy in food	AT2 Level 2
75	Something made from…	To identify a range of common materials. To understand that the same material can be used to make different objects.	This is a straightforward observation sheet. The question at the end is best dealt with during class discussion.	Science NC: Sc3 Grouping and classifying materials QCA: Unit 3C Characteristics of materials	SCN 013X – Properties and uses	AT1 Level 2 AT3 Level 2
76	Material match	To know properties of materials such as hardness and flexibility. To understand that some materials are suitable for making a particular object because of these properties.	Introduce the term 'properties'. Children should be told that they can use more than one word to describe each object and that the same word can be used for more than one object illustrated.	Science NC: Sc3 Grouping and classifying materials QCA: Unit 3C Characteristics of materials	SCN 013X – Properties and uses	AT1 Level 2 AT3 Level 2
77	Where are the rocks?	To learn that beneath all land surfaces there is rock.	Colouring pencils would be useful here. Ensure that children know that stones and pebbles are small pieces of rock.	Science NC: Sc3 Grouping and classifying materials QCA: Unit 3D Rocks and soils	SCN 0002B – Biodiversity	AT3 Level 2
78	Natural attraction	To make and test predictions about whether materials are magnetic or not.	First children record their predictions. Provide the equipment and objects listed. Children then carry out the experiment and record their results. Note that all objects attracted to magnets are made of metal but not all objects made of metal are attracted to magnets. Iron, steel, nickel and cobalt and objects containing these metals are attracted to magnets.	Science NC: Sc4 Forces and motion QCA: Unit 3E Magnets and springs	SCN 008L; SCN 110L– Forces and motion	AT1 Level 2 AT3 Level 2
79	Springs	To understand that springs are used in a variety of ways.	Show the class some springs. Note that the pen is retractable and uses a spring. The last question requires some investigation and suitable reference books.	Science NC: Sc4 Forces and motion QCA: Unit 3E Magnets and springs	SCN 008L – Forces and motion	AT1 Level 2 AT4 Level 2
80	Which way?	To understand that forces act in particular directions.	This activity tests children's understanding of directional force and of forces working in opposite directions to revise. The terms 'push' and 'pull' must be understood.	Science NC: Sc4 Forces and motion QCA: Unit 2E Forces and movement	SCN 007L – Forces and motion	AT4 Level 1/2
81	OTT	To understand the properties 'opaque', 'translucent' and 'transparent' and how they are defined in terms of the transmission of light.	Encourage children to use the correct terms (they will enjoy knowing the long words). The mirror is a trick item as it is, of course, opaque but also reflect light – a different concept, which can be discussed.	Science NC: Sc3 Grouping and classifying materials QCA: Unit 3C Characteristics of materials	SCN 115X – Properties and uses	AT1 Level 2 AT3 Level 2/3
82	Shapely shadows	To know that shadows are formed when an object blocks the light source. To understand that shadows formed by objects in sunlight, change position according to the time of day.	This is an experiment requiring two or more children and it also requires time. In class discussion of the experiment emphasise that when sunlight is behind an object the shadow is in front.	Science NC: Sc4 The Earth and beyond QCA: Unit 3F Light and shadows	SCN 105E – Astronomy	AT1 Level 2 AT4 Level 2/3

NO FUSS
PHOTOCOPIABLE

SCHOLASTIC
www.scholastic.co.uk

Page	Activity	Objectives	Teachers' notes	NC, QCA & Primary Framework	Curriculum for Excellence (Scotland)	AT links and levels
83	The sundial	To understand that shadows can be used to tell the time. To learn how to make a sundial.	Making the sundial is straightforward; the tricky bit is the making of reasonable calibrations against clock time. The sundial needs to stay put!	Science NC: Sc4 The Earth and beyond QCA: Unit 3F Light and shadows	SCN 105E – Astronomy	AT1 Level 2 AT4 Level 2/3
84	A Roman legionary	To begin to understand why the Romans were successful in their invasion of Britain.	This should be used as reinforcement for historical topic work. Legionaries were also engineers, clerks, medical orderlies, musicians and standard-bearers. Overall the Romans used about 50,000 men to subdue Britain.	History NC: Knowledge and understanding of events, people and changes in the past; Breadth of study QCA: Unit 6A Why have people invaded and settled in Britain…	SOC 104E – People, past events and societies	AT Level 2
85	Roman mosaics	To find out about the effect of Roman settlement on Britain.	Mosaics are one of the legacies of Roman settlement. See originals if possible. Enlarge the sheet if it helps. Make s ure that plenty of books are available with information on Roman mosaics.	History NC: Knowledge and understanding of events, people and changes in the past; Breadth of study QCA: Unit 6A Why have people invaded and settled in Britain…	SOC 104E – People, past events and societies	AT Level 2
86	Public baths	To understand about life in Roman Britain from a number of sources.	Reference material should support this work. The letter is a précis of one sent by Seneca the Younger from his flat in Rome to his friend Lucilius. Interrogate the evidence for information. Try to turn the perceived disadvantages into selling points.	History NC: Knowledge and understanding of events, people and changes in the past; Breadth of study QCA: Unit 6A Why have people invaded and settled in Britain…	SOC 203C – People, past events and societies	AT Level 2/3
87	It's a riddle	To find out about the way of life of Anglo-Saxons.	Ask children if they know any riddles. The originals of these riddles were written between 950 and AD 1000. (The pictures provide the answers.)	History NC: Knowledge and understanding of events, people and changes in the past; Romans, Anglo-Saxons and Vikings in Britain QCA: Unit 6A Why have people invaded and settled in Britain…	SOC 002C – People, past events and societies	AT Level 2/3
88	Saxon dress	To learn about the way of life of Anglo-Saxons: how they dressed.	Discuss how we know about clothes in the past (from archaeological evidence). The colours 'woad' (bright blue), 'weld' (bright yellow) and 'madder' (red) could be mixed to make other colours.	History NC: Knowledge and understanding of events, people and changes in the past; Romans, Anglo-Saxons and Vikings in Britain QCA: Unit 6A Why have people invaded and settled in Britain…	SOC 103C – People, past events and societies	AT Level 2/3
89	A Viking longboat	To learn about Viking longboats.	Longboats (or longships – both terms are used) varied in size according to the task for which they were designed. The prow of one ship (Gokstad) was carved with a dragon's head.	History NC: Knowledge and understanding of events, people and changes in the past; Romans, Anglo-Saxons and Vikings in Britain QCA: Unit 6A Why have people invaded and settled in Britain…	SOC 201A – People, past events and societies	AT Level 2/3
90	Where Vikings settled	To investigate where the Vikings settled in Britain.	Introduce the notion of place names having shared endings (Portsmouth, Lossiemouth and so on). To complete the exercise a fairly detailed map of Britain is required: a road atlas is ideal.	History NC: Knowledge and understanding of events, people and changes in the past; Romans, Anglo-Saxons and Vikings in Britain QCA: Unit 6A Why have people invaded and settled in Britain…	SOC 201A – People, past events and societies	AT Level 2/3
91	A kenning shield	To understand what a Viking kenning is.	Explain by example what a 'kenning' is (for example, a train might be an iron horse). Acknowledge imagination and invention in completing the task. Make a display of the best kennings.	History NC: Knowledge and understanding of events, people and changes in the past; Romans, Anglo-Saxons and Vikings in Britain QCA: Unit 6A Why have people invaded and settled in Britain…	SOC 201A – People, past events and societies	AT Level 2/3
92	Job sort	To classify types of work.	Explain what the categories are; use the term 'sets' if the children are familiar with it. Discussion is important as the classification of some occupations is a matter of opinion.	Geography NC: Geographical enquiry and skills QCA: Unit 6 Investigating our local area	SOC 007M – People, place and environment	AT Level 2
93	Climate	To identify hot and cold places on a map or globe.	Introduce words such as 'climate', 'mild', 'globe' and 'equator'. Talk with children about any hot or cold places they may have visited, heard about, or seen in films. Colouring should be done lightly.	Geography NC: Knowledge and understanding of places QCA: Unit 7: Weather around the world	SOC 111J – People, place and environment	AT Level 2
94	Happy holidays (1)	To understand how climate affects human activity.	Interrogate the picture. Ask: Where is it? What is it like there? What sort of activities would you do in a place like this? Talk about climate and why people choose to go on holiday in different places. Simple world maps or atlases are useful for this exercise.	Geography NC: Geographical enquiry and skills; Knowledge and understanding of places QCA: Unit 7: Weather around the world	SOC 111J – People, place and environment SOC 212J – People, place and environment	AT Level 2

Page	Activity	Objectives	Teachers' notes	NC, QCA & Primary Framework	Curriculum for Excellence (Scotland)	AT links and levels
95	Happy holidays (2)	To understand how climate affects human activity.	Interrogate the picture and complete the sheet as above.	Geography NC: Geographical enquiry and skills; Knowledge and understanding of places QCA: Unit 7: Weather around the world	SOC 111J – People, place and environment SOC 212J – People, place and environment	AT Level 2
96	Where did it happen?	To investigate places using secondary sources.	Children should read the headlines and the text and note where each event is taking place. They should find the places on a map of Britain.	Geography NC: Geographical enquiry and skills; Knowledge and understanding QCA: Unit 6 Investigating our local area	SOC 214L – People, place and environment	AT Level 2/3
97	Packing for a purpose	To investigate how materials have been used to make packaging fit for purpose and to consider stiffness and stability in design.	Accompany this sheet with hands-on examination of real cereal packets. The answer to the second question is not simply 'cereal': there is usually some secondary packaging. Use vocabulary such as 'packaging', 'edge', 'face', 'adhesive', 'join' and 'capacity'.	Design and technology NC: Breadth of study QCA: Unit 3A Packaging	TCH 205C – Technologies	AT Level 1
98	Nets (1)	To learn that a 3D shape can be constructed from a net (a 2D plan) and that the 3D shape depends upon the shape of the net. To develop skills in cutting, scoring and assembling.	Talk about nets. Discuss and demonstrate the activity and the skills (especially scoring) involved. Make the necessary safety statements.	Design and technology NC: Knowledge and understanding of materials and components QCA: Unit 3A Packaging	TCH 205C – Technologies	AT Level 2
99	Nets (2)	To understand that a 3D shape can be constructed from a net and that the 3D shape depends upon the shape of the net.	This is looking at the same concept as the previous sheet but starting from the finished 3D object (polyhedron).	Design and technology NC: Knowledge and understanding of materials and components QCA: Unit 3A Packaging	TCH 205C – Technologies	AT Level 2
100	Design and make	To learn how to create a package for a given purpose and to consider the need to make designs stable.	There is a lot involved in completing this sheet fully and equipment for making will be required. Make sure the instructions are understood.	Design and technology NC: Developing, planning and communicating ideas; Working with tools QCA: Unit 3A Packaging	TCH 207D; TCH 208D; TCH 209E – Technologies	AT Level 2/3
101	Sandwich selection	To recognise that different sandwiches are created for different needs, occasions and purposes.	Reference material will be required. Instead of inserting drawings of their own, children could use pictures printed from the computer or magazine cuttings. You may consider using this sheet as a basis for a design and make exercise.	Design and technology NC: Developing, planning and communicating ideas QCA: Unit 3B Sandwich snacks	TCH 202A; TCH 209E – Technologies	AT Level 2
102	Pneumatic gnome	To develop an understanding of a simple pneumatic system and to construct one that works.	Try this at home first. Collect the materials that will be needed. A great deal of discussion needs to take place if the gnome is to pop up. Ask: What will the gnome be made of? (Alternatively you could open the lid of a box or send Santa up the chimney instead.) There are a number of practical challenges to be solved.	Design and technology NC: Working with tools, equipment, materials and components; Evaluating processes and products QCA: Unit 3C Moving monsters	TCH 201A – Technologies	AT Level 2/3
103	Fitting fonts	To learn how to alter font size, type and colour for emphasis and effect.	Although it is clear what is expected here, there are no definitive answers: it is a matter of judgement as to which style suits the purpose. Children may be asked to justify their choices.	ICT NC: Exchanging and sharing information QCA: Unit 3A Combining text and graphics	TCH 212G; TCH 216K – Technologies	AT Level 1/2
104	Business card mix-up	To learn how graphics and text are combined to communicate information.	Show a few genuine business cards so that children appreciate what the sheet is all about. You may need to recap how to locate, retrieve and add graphics to text using a computer.	ICT NC: Developing ideas and making things happen QCA: Unit 3A Combining text and graphics	TCH 212G; TCH 216K – Technologies	AT Level 2
105	Book cover	To learn how graphics and text are combined to communicate information.	This is a more sophisticated form of the exercise on the previous sheet.	ICT NC: Developing ideas and making things happen QCA: Unit 3A Combining text and graphics	TCH 212G; TCH 216K – Technologies	AT Level 2
106	Computer glossary	To become more familiar with technical vocabulary.	The ability to read fairly demanding text is required. You may wish to undertake this task orally.	ICT NC: Developing ideas and making things happen; Exchanging and sharing information QCA: Unit 3A Combining text and graphics	TCH 212G; TCH 213H; TCH 216K – Technologies	AT Level 2

SCHOLASTIC
www.scholastic.co.uk

Page	Activity	Objectives	Teachers' notes	NC, QCA & Primary Framework	Curriculum for Excellence (Scotland)	AT links and levels
107	More than one (1)	To comment on and compare approaches to group portrait work.	This is companion to the sheet below but should be attempted first. It is important to talk about the relationships between the people. Ask: How can you tell what it is? How is the relationship shown by the artist? (Look at pose, position, dress and expression.)	Art and design; NC: Exploring and developing ideas; Evaluating and developing work; QCA: Unit 3A Portraying relationships	EXA 105E – Art and design	AT Level 2
108	More than one (2)	To comment on and compare approaches to group portrait work. To explore how to create a portrait showing the relationship between two people.	See the above notes. You will need to assess what skills the children bring to the last exercise: for example, can they mix paint to produce tints?	Art and design; NC: Exploring and developing ideas; Evaluating and developing work; QCA: Unit 3A Portraying relationships	EXA 105E; EXA 208G – Art and design	AT Level 2
109	Patterns	To explore ways of making and developing patterns.	Key words should be learned: 'geometric'; 'shapes'; 'symmetry'; 'reflection'; 'rotation'; 'transform'; 'translate' and 'repeat'. Scissors and glue are needed as are lots of repeats of their own shape.	Art and design; NC: Investigating and making art, craft and design; QCA: Unit 3B Investigating pattern	EXA 106F; EXA 005E – Art and design	AT Level 2
110	What difference does it make?	To learn to question and make thoughtful observations about how sculptors' work can improve the quality of an environment.	Photographs, film – even a walk down the high street to look for sculpture, can help to make this exercise real. The sheet itself is self-explanatory.	Art and design; NC: Knowledge and understanding; QCA: Unit 3C Can we change places?	EXA 106F – Art and design	AT Level 2
111	The frog and the snake (1)	To explore descriptive sounds. To learn how to musically interpret text and illustrations. To combine narration and sound to describe particular animals.	This sheet and the next should be used together, although you may choose to divide the exercise into sections. Children should first listen to some descriptive animal music such as Respighi's The Birds, or Saint-Saëns' The Carnival of the Animals. Note that the musical description should not be limited to what is mentioned in the text; the pictures can evoke other sounds.	Music; NC: Controlling sounds through singing and playing; Creating and developing musical ideas; QCA: Unit 9 Animal magic	EXA 113Q – Music	AT Level 1/2
112	The frog and the snake (2)	To explore descriptive sounds. To learn how to musically interpret text and illustrations. To combine narration and sound to describe particular animals.	See notes above.	Music; NC: Controlling sounds through singing and playing; Creating and developing musical ideas; QCA: Unit 9 Animal magic	EXA 113Q – Music	AT Level 1/2
113	Ostinati	To learn to perform a repeated rhythmic pattern to a steady pulse.	Use and explain the term 'ostinato' (a repeated pattern – once is not enough). Listen to an example, such as Mike Oldfield's Tubular Bells.	Music; NC: Creating and developing musical ideas; QCA: Unit 10 Play it again	EXA 114X – Music	AT Level 2
114	Signs and symbols	To explore the difference between signs and symbols.	There is a certain amount of overlap between the two words but generally a sign has one clearly accessible meaning and a symbol often requires further knowledge to understand its meaning. The cross, star and dove are most clearly symbols.	RE; Non-statutory framework: Learning about religion; QCA: Unit 3A What do signs and symbols mean in religion?		Non-statutory AT1 Level 1
115	Objects and memories	To examine how memories can be linked to particular objects.	Try to bring into the classroom an object that triggers some good memories for you and share these with the class. The discussion – and the sheet activity – can follow naturally from this.	RE; Non-statutory framework: Learning about religion; QCA: Unit 3A What do signs and symbols mean in religion?		Non-statutory AT1 Level 1
116	Passover	To learn about the significance of Passover in Judaism.	This sheet cannot be used 'cold'. Passover (Pesach) recalls the escape from slavery in Egypt around 3300 years ago. Ask children what sort of meal they would prepare to remind them of home.	RE; Non-statutory framework: Learning about religion; Breadth of study (Religions and beliefs); QCA: Unit 3A What do signs and symbols mean in religion?		Non-statutory AT1 Level 2; AT2 Level 2
117	The Passover meal	To learn how symbolic food can be used to remember important events.	Before starting this sheet, the children will need to know the background to a Seder meal and Passover. They judge which parts of the story each food represents. Bitter herbs (the misery of slavery), matzah (slaves getting crumbs of food to live), eggs (new life after slavery), charoset (the mortar used by slaves to build for their Egyptian masters). See www.judaism.about.com.	RE; Non-statutory framework: Learning about religion; Breadth of study (Religions and beliefs); QCA: Unit 3A What do signs and symbols mean in religion?		Non-statutory AT1 Level 2

Page	Activity	Objectives	Teachers' notes	NC, QCA & Primary Framework	Curriculum for Excellence (Scotland)	AT links and levels
118	More than they say	To understand how metaphors can convey religious meaning.	Have a discussion before using this sheet. Talk through some idioms – 'It's raining cats and dogs'; 'Milly is driving me up the wall' – and distinguish between the literal meaning and the non-literal. Check with your RE coordinator or vicar if you cannot explain the Christian phrases on the sheet.	RE Non-statutory framework: Learning from religion; Breadth of study (Themes) QCA: Unit 3A What do signs and symbols mean in religion?		Non-statutory AT1 Level 2 AT2 Level 2
119	Diwali cards	To identify some features of Diwali.	Diwali runs for five days, usually in October or November. Information about Diwali is available at: www.diwalimela.com.	RE Non-statutory framework: Learning about religion; Breadth of study (Religions and beliefs) QCA: Unit 3A What do signs and symbols mean in religion?		Non-statutory AT1 Level 2
120	Find out about the Bible	To glean some basic information about the Bible and why it is important to Christians.	This is a test sheet – a straightforward cloze procedure. The teaching needs to have taken place before the sheet is employed.	RE Non-statutory framework: Breadth of study (Religions and beliefs; Themes)		Non-statutory AT1 Level 2
121	Saving for something special	To know why saving money is necessary and to understand about basic ways of saving.	In the one blank daydream bubble, encourage children to draw something that they would save up for. On the sheet, options D and E are clearly the best. Discuss the other options: Why is it not a good idea to hide money under the bed?	PSHE and Citizenship NC guidelines: Developing confidence and responsibility and making the most of their abilities QCA: Unit 2 Choices		N/A
122	Jobs: likes and dislikes (1)	To know a range of jobs and work roles and to be aware of what people might like or dislike about undertaking them.	The activities on this and the next three pages are intended to increase children's awareness of how society works. Talk about the roles played by people they know (mum, dad, teacher). List useful words such as: 'proud', 'tired', 'interesting', 'enjoyable' and so on. Children could research the activities shown in groups.	PSHE and Citizenship NC guidelines: Developing good relationships and respecting the differences between people QCA: Unit 5 Living in a diverse world		N/A
123	Jobs: likes and dislikes (2)	To know a range of jobs and work roles and to be aware of what people might like or dislike about undertaking them.	See notes above.	PSHE and Citizenship NC guidelines: Developing good relationships and respecting the differences between people QCA: Unit 5 Living in a diverse world		N/A
124	Jobs: likes and dislikes (3)	To know a range of jobs and work roles and to be aware of what people might like or dislike about undertaking them.	See notes above.	PSHE and Citizenship NC guidelines: Developing good relationships and respecting the differences between people QCA: Unit 5 Living in a diverse world		N/A
125	Jobs: likes and dislikes (4)	To know a range of jobs and work roles and to be aware of what people might like or dislike about undertaking them.	See notes above.	PSHE and Citizenship NC guidelines: Developing good relationships and respecting the differences between people QCA: Unit 5 Living in a diverse world		N/A
126	Beating bullying	To consider why it is wrong to bully and explore strategies for dealing with bullying.	This subject is not as straightforward as it seems. You must discuss questions such as: What is bullying? How do we recognise it?. Children may prefer to work in pairs to complete the sheet. When discussing afterwards, make the talk as positive as possible. (Consult any guidelines that are available in your school.)	PSHE and Citizenship NC guidelines: Developing good relationships and respecting the differences between people		N/A
127	Looking after yourself	To be aware of health and hygiene issues and to understand their responsibility for personal cleanliness.	Personal hygiene can be a sensitive issue so you may opt to tackle this in an academic way. Ask: What would be the perfect hygiene regime? Can you make up rules for teachers to follow?	PSHE and Citizenship NC guidelines: Developing a healthy, safer lifestyle		N/A

NO FUSS
PHOTOCOPIABLE

Words in words

How many words can you find in…

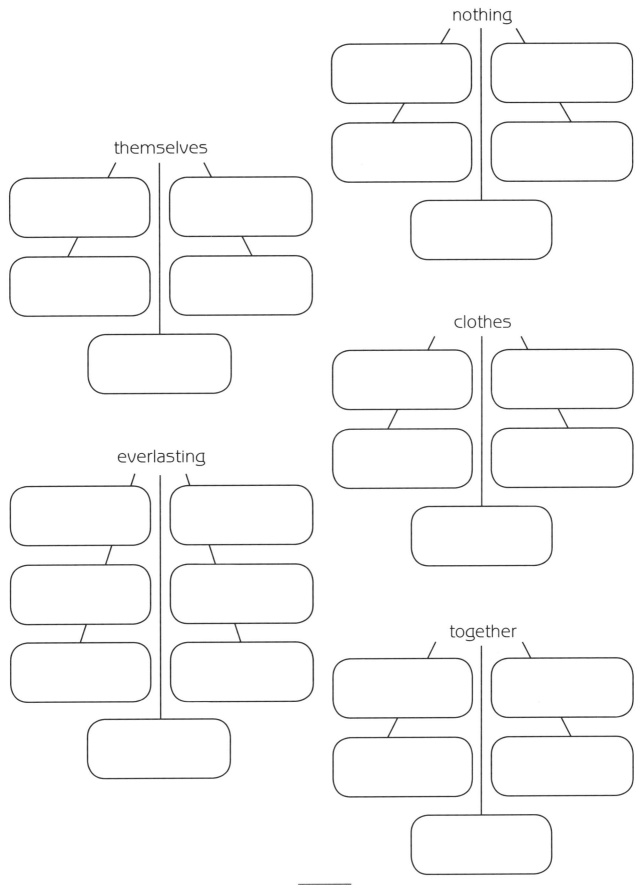

nothing

themselves

everlasting

clothes

together

Name _____

Compounds in the playground

Find as many compound words as you can in this picture.

NO FUSS
PHOTOCOPIABLE

New words for old

Make new compound words to replace these words. The first one has been done for you.

	word		new word
	vest	→	chestcosy
	pram	→	
	kettle	→	
	bird	→	
	camel	→	
	skates	→	
	watch	→	

Name _____

The silence in lambs

Lam**ⓑ** has a silent letter **ⓑ**.

● Say these words, then circle the silent letters.

write   lamb   gnat

wrong   knife   know

wring

sign   wriggle

gnaw   hymn

bomb

knee   rhyme

● Can you find more words with silent letters?

Word blender

Make words and non-words, and list them in the table. One has been done as an example.

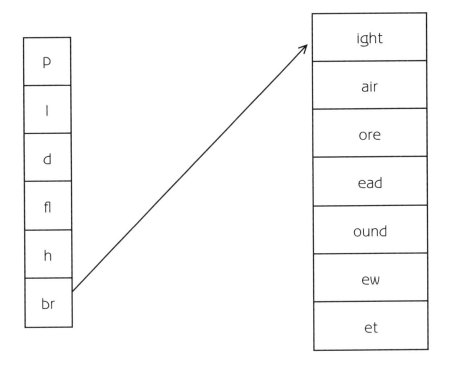

Words	Non-words
bright	

Name _____

Put back the missing 'le'

Someone has made a **mudd le** by cutting **le** off the ends of words.

Put them back in where they belong.

Doctor Foster fell in a pudd   up to his midd   .

Didd   didd   dumpling, my son John...

The cat and the fidd   , the cow jumped over the moon.

When the wind blows, the crad   will rock.

Litt   Miss Muffet sat on a tuffet.

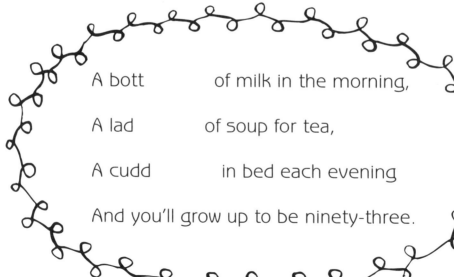

A bott   of milk in the morning,

A lad   of soup for tea,

A cudd   in bed each evening

And you'll grow up to be ninety-three.

NO FUSS
PHOTOCOPIABLE

Name _____

'Re' chart

Complete this chart using the prefix **re** to make new words. Add one of your own at the bottom. Think about what the new words mean.

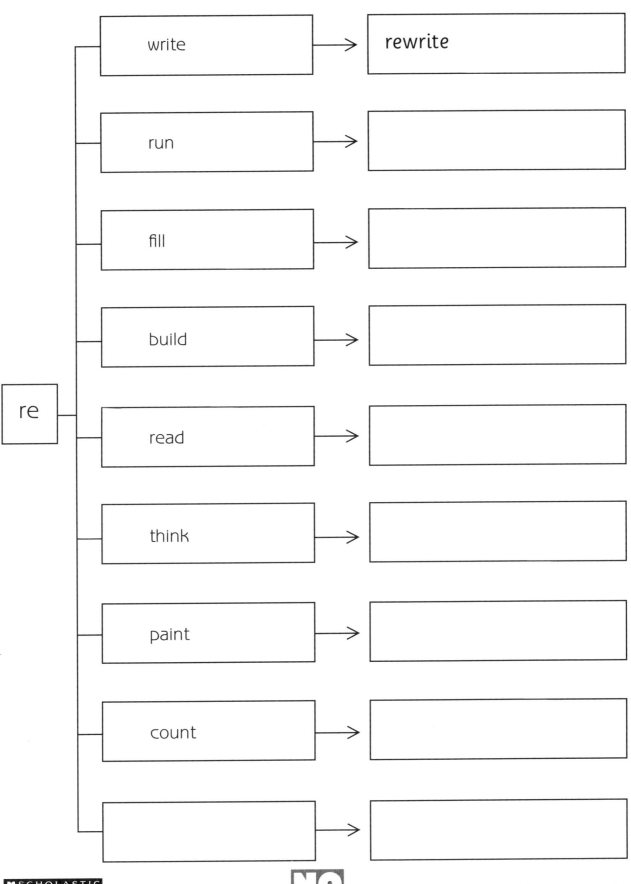

re		
write	→	rewrite
run	→	
fill	→	
build	→	
read	→	
think	→	
paint	→	
count	→	
	→	

NO FUSS
PHOTOCOPIABLE

Name _____

'Un' web

● Complete this web using the prefix **un**. Think about what the new words mean.
● Add one of your own.

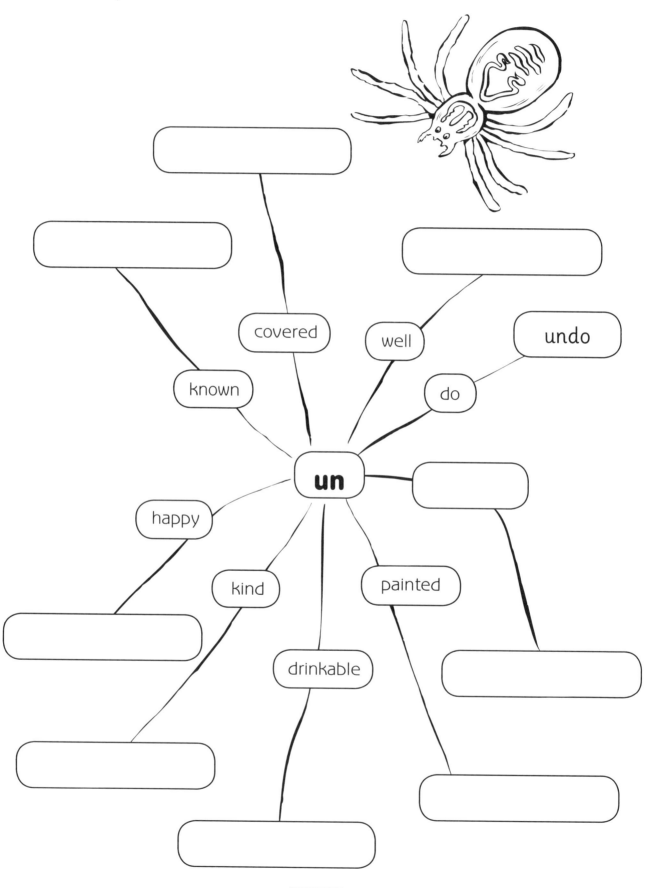

un

covered

well

undo

known

do

happy

kind

painted

drinkable

Where's 'y'?

Use the suffix **y** to make sense of these sentences. Write them out correctly.
Watch out – the root word sometimes changes.

It was a **cloud** day.

_____

The clown was very **fun**.

_____

My fish seemed very **smell**.

_____

We picnicked on the **grass** bank.

_____

Our cat has a **bone** back.

_____

The **noise** jet zoomed overhead.

_____

Name _____

Weather forecast

The suffix **y** is used often in this weather forecast. Write out the root words.

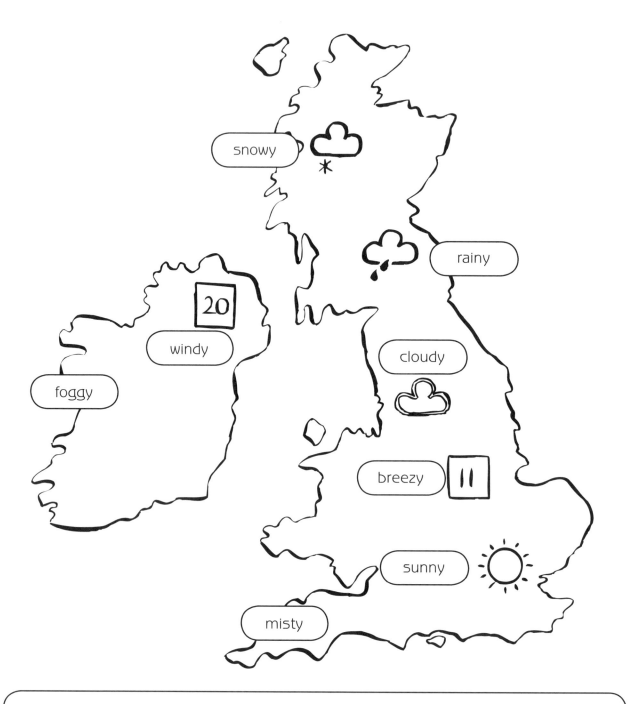

snowy

rainy

20

windy

cloudy

foggy

breezy 11

sunny

misty

Root words

m _____ f _____ su _____ sn _____

w _____ c _____ r _____ b _____

Suffix chains

● These words use the suffixes **ful** and **less**. Write the missing root-word link.

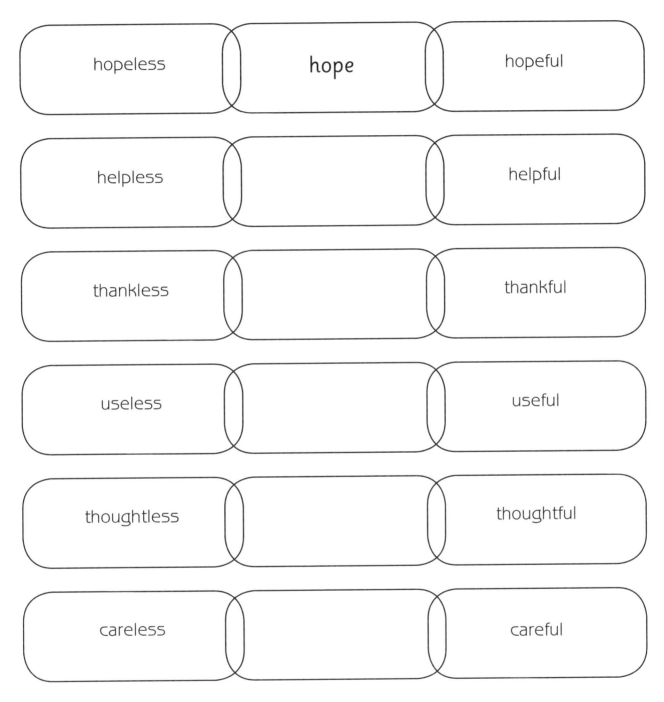

hopeless	hope	hopeful
helpless		helpful
thankless		thankful
useless		useful
thoughtless		thoughtful
careless		careful

● Write a chain of your own.

NO FUSS
PHOTOCOPIABLE

Name _____

Fixing suffixes

● Fix the suffixes **er** and **est** to these words. The first one has been done for you.

| wide | wider | widest |

| close | | |

| small | | |

| happy | | |

| sad | | |

● Add **er** and **est** to a word of your own.

Step on the verb

Colour over the verbs to help the pirate reach the treasure.

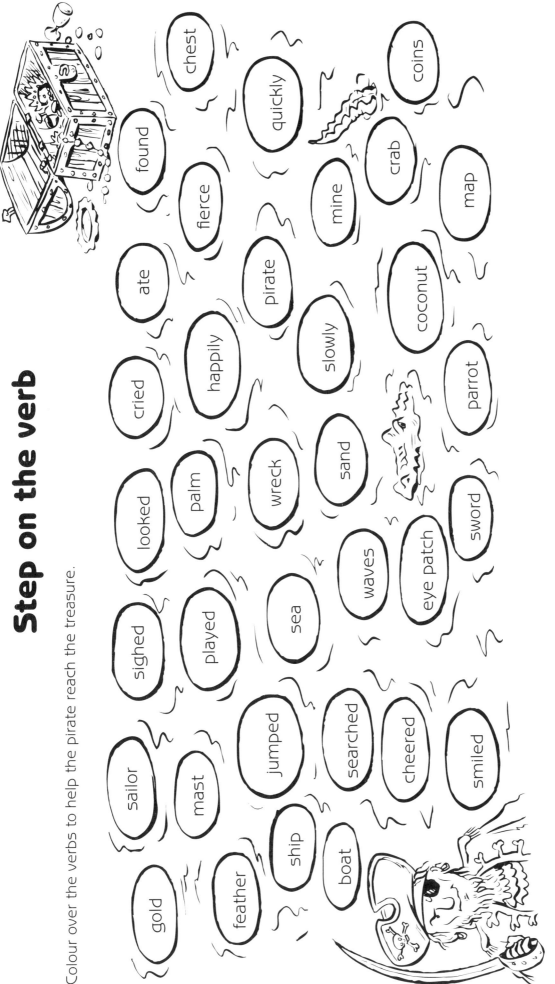

chest

quickly

coins

found

fierce

mine

crab

map

ate

pirate

coconut

cried

happily

slowly

parrot

looked

palm

wreck

sand

sword

sighed

played

sea

waves

eye patch

sailor

mast

jumped

searched

cheered

smiled

gold

feather

ship

boat

The pirate **smiled,** _____ _____

and **found** the treasure. _____

Where's the verb?

Put in the missing verb so that these sentences make sense.

Jack and Jill up the hill.

_____

Mary a little lamb.

_____

Little Jack Horner in a corner.

_____

Who Cock Robin?

_____

Humpty Dumpty on a wall.

_____

I with my little eye…

_____

Hickory dickory dock
The mouse up the clock.

_____

NO FUSS
PHOTOCOPIABLE

Name _____

'ing' wheel

When you add **ing** to a verb, the spelling of the verb sometimes changes. Add **ing** to these words and put the new words in the correct list.

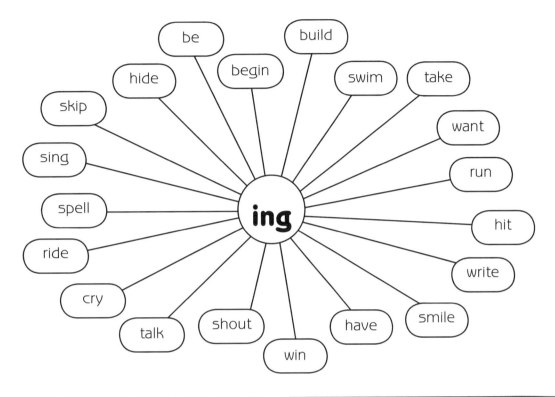

Change	No change
riding	spelling

Name _____

Computer error

This computer can only use **said** when reporting speech. Replace **said** with better verbs.

"Help!" **said** the girl as she fell into the sea.

A man **said**, "Call the coastguard!"

"Where is the lifebelt?" **said** the woman on the pier.

"Help! Help!" the girl **said** again as the waves

crashed over her head.

Her friend was crying. "I told her not to do a

handstand on the rocks," she **said**.

"Keep calm!" **said** the policeman. "I'm

coming." He dived into the sea. "Hold on to my

waist," he **said** above the noise of the waves.

At that moment the fin of a shark appeared. "Oh no," **said** her friend.

The watching crowd **said**, "Hurry!"

Helpful verbs

(shouted) (cried) (asked) (exclaimed) (called) (commanded)

(enquired) (instructed) (muttered) (repeated) (screamed)

Synonym search

Synonyms are words that share the same or similar meanings, for example:
small and **little**,
shout and **yell**.

How many synonyms for **nice** can you find in this puzzle?

a	e	n	j	o	y	a	b	l	e
x	y	t	t	e	r	p	p	d	l
l	o	v	e	l	y	o	e	o	v
b	c	u	r	n	w	l	n	x	o
r	y	b	r	c	s	i	i	s	m
d	e	l	i	g	h	t	f	u	l
w	n	t	f	v	o	e	m	p	n
s	c	i	l	l	i	o	q	e	t
s	r	z	c	b	c	y	d	r	a
d	i	d	n	e	l	p	s	b	s

PHOTOCOPIABLE

Name _____

Lists of opposites

Antonyms are words with opposite meanings, for example **hot** and **cold**, **up** and **down**.
Use a thesaurus and a dictionary to find as many antonyms as you can for these words.

happy	big
unhappy sad miserable	

polite	weak

NO FUSS
PHOTOCOPIABLE

DIY dictionary

Write and illustrate your own dictionary.

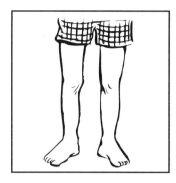

leg <u>in humans, one of two lower limbs, used</u>
<u>for moving and holding up the body</u>

lemon _____

_____

_____

_____

letter _____

_____

_____

_____

life-jacket _____

_____

_____

_____

lion _____

_____

_____

_____

Name _____

The long and short of it

An **apostrophe** can be used to replace a letter or letters and so shorten a word. Complete the chart.

▬ becomes ➡			apostrophe (') replaces
do not	➡	don't	o
will not	➡		
would not	➡		
cannot	➡		
are not	➡		
it is	➡		
there is	➡		
who is	➡		
he is	➡		
she is	➡		

SCHOLASTIC
www.scholastic.co.uk

Making plurals

● Complete these lists of plurals.

One apple, many __apples__

One bag, many _____

One cup, many _____

One dog, many _____

One egg, many _____

One frog, many _____

One goat, many _____

● How did you make these plurals?

A box – some __boxes__

A church – some _____

A dish – some _____

A fox – some _____

A glass – some _____

A dress – some _____

A wish – some _____

● How did you make these plurals?

● How do these plurals work?

story ➡ _____   baby ➡ _____

fairy ➡ _____   lady ➡ _____

body ➡ _____   party ➡ _____

Name _____

Odd plurals

What are the plurals?

a sheep

some _____

one half

two _____

a man

several _____

a child

many _____

one tooth

lots of _____

one fish

many _____

a mouse

some _____

■ SCHOLASTIC
www.scholastic.co.uk

Ten to Tooting

● Read and finish this poem. Listen for the sounds at the start of the words.
● Illustrate your poem in the frame.

One wiggly worm,

Two terrible toads,

Three _____,

Four _____,

Five _____,

Six _____,

Seven _____,

Eight _____,

Nine _____,

Ten _____,

turned up in Tooting.

Tooting

Confusing cuttings (1)

Read these cuttings. Which are fiction and which are non-fiction? Explain how you can tell.

 The woodcutter took his axe and chopped down the door. Then he started on Grandma. Luckily, Grandma was really the wolf in her nightie. So Little Red Riding Hood was safe and the wolf was dead.

_____

_____

Wolves hunt together in packs. They are dog-like animals with grey fur and upright ears. They are carnivorous.

_____

_____

On Wednesday, Manchester United had a lucky escape. They were saved from defeat by Nantes when they scored a penalty in extra time.

_____

_____

The sky glowed red. A green creature appeared from behind a rock. In the red light it was beautiful and horrible at the same time. Its legs and arms were tied in a confused knot. Then it spoke: "Take me to your leader."

_____

_____

NO FUSS
PHOTOCOPIABLE

Confusing cuttings (2)

Can you tell non-fiction from fiction? Explain how.

Put the fish in the pan. Pour 1 pint of stock over it and boil for 20 minutes.

_____

_____

Most teachers know how to teach spelling, but need to spend more time on teaching sentence-level skills.

_____

_____

In the corner was a seat. Jack sat on it with a Christmas pie on his lap. He had forgotten his spoon, so had to use his thumb instead. He stuck a plumb on his thumb and said, "What a good boy am I?"

_____

_____

Most modern cars use unleaded petrol. This helps to keep the air cleaner, which is a good thing for us and the environment in general.

_____

_____

Name _____

Off-the-peg rhymes

Use the items on the washing line to complete the rhyming poem.

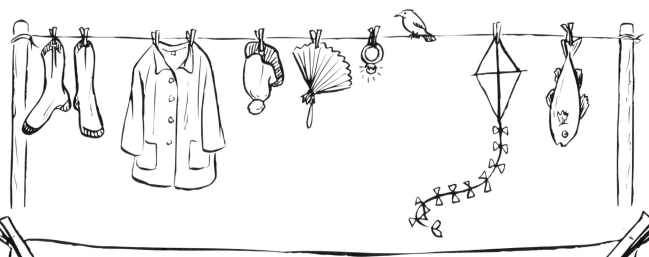

On Sunday...

Oliver White flew a _____

Britney Cox wore long _____

Manjit Singh found a _____

Emma Catt ate her _____

James and Trish caught a _____

Simon Groat sold his _____

Lisa Tan flapped her _____

Sarah Hird caught a _____

Then they went to bed.

Name _____

Crash chaos

Look carefully at the photograph and write a newspaper report to go with it.

Name _____

Keeping count

In ones

● Fill in the gaps on this number line.

				145	146	147	148		

● Count **on** 8 from…

200 → □   136 → □   71 → □   252 → □

● Count **back** 13 from…

140 → □   167 → □   216 → □   331 → □

In tens

1	2	3	4	5	6	7	8	9	10
11	12	13	14	15	16	17	18	19	20
21	22	23	24	25	26	27	28	29	30
31	32	33	34	35	36	37	38	39	40
41	42	43	44	45	46	47	48	49	50
51	52	53	54	55	56	57	58	59	60
61	62	63	64	65	66	67	68	69	70
71	72	73	74	75	76	77	78	79	80
81	82	83	84	85	86	87	88	89	90
91	92	93	94	95	96	97	98	99	100

● Count **on** in tens…   starting with 10. Colour the squares.
     starting with 3. Colour the squares.

● Count **back** in tens…   starting with 98. Colour the squares.
     starting with 91. Colour the squares.

█ SCHOLASTIC
www.scholastic.co.uk

Big steps

● Make the next steps.

153 · 163 · 173 · ○ · ○ · ○ · ○

122 · 222 · 322 · ○ · ○ · ○ · ○

600 · 500 · 400 · ○ · ○ · ○ · ○

135 · 125 · 115 · ○ · ○ · ○ · ○

● Complete the number ladder.

1. What number will the top step be?

2. What number is the fifth step?

1560

1460

1360

Name _____

The missing thinks

- Complete these sequences.
- Write down the rule for each one.

 5 10 15   25

_____

 4 7 10   19

_____

 58 56 54

_____

 1   11 16   26

_____

 39 35   27 23

_____

Name _____

Multiples

Two four six eight
I saw a pixie on a gate.

● Lightly colour all the multiples of 2.

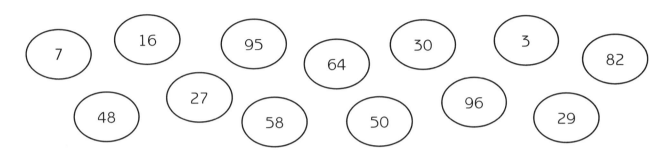

7 16 95 30 3
64 82
48 27 58 50 96 29

Five ten fifteen twenty
I think one meal a day is plenty.

● Colour in the multiples of 5.

22 63
15 90 31
50
35 70 54 45
88

● Write three multiples of 100. _____ _____ _____

● Write three multiples of 50. _____ _____ _____

● Write three multiples of 5. _____ _____ _____

● Multiples of 50 end in [   ] or [   ].

Name _____

Boxed in

		H		T		U
457 is		4	and	5	and	7

457 =   400   +   50   +   7

● Let these numbers out of their boxes into…

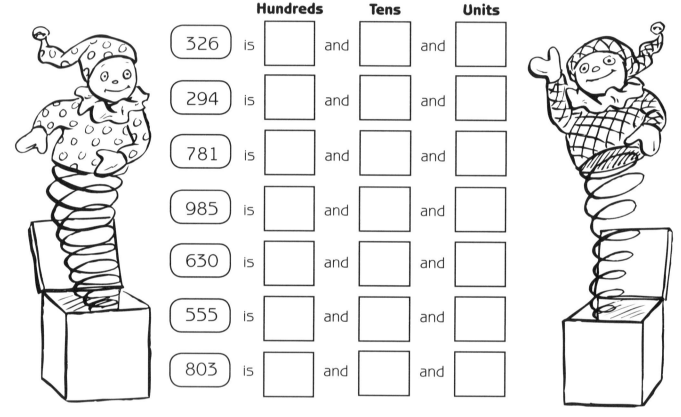

		Hundreds		Tens		Units
326	is		and		and	
294	is		and		and	
781	is		and		and	
985	is		and		and	
630	is		and		and	
555	is		and		and	
803	is		and		and	

● Complete these number sentences.

432 = ☐ + 30 + 2

697 = 600 + ☐ + 7

785 = 700 + 80 + ☐

831 = 800 + 30 + ☐

249 = 200 + ☐ + 9

■ SCHOLASTIC
www.scholastic.co.uk

Piggy in the middle

What number is halfway between these?

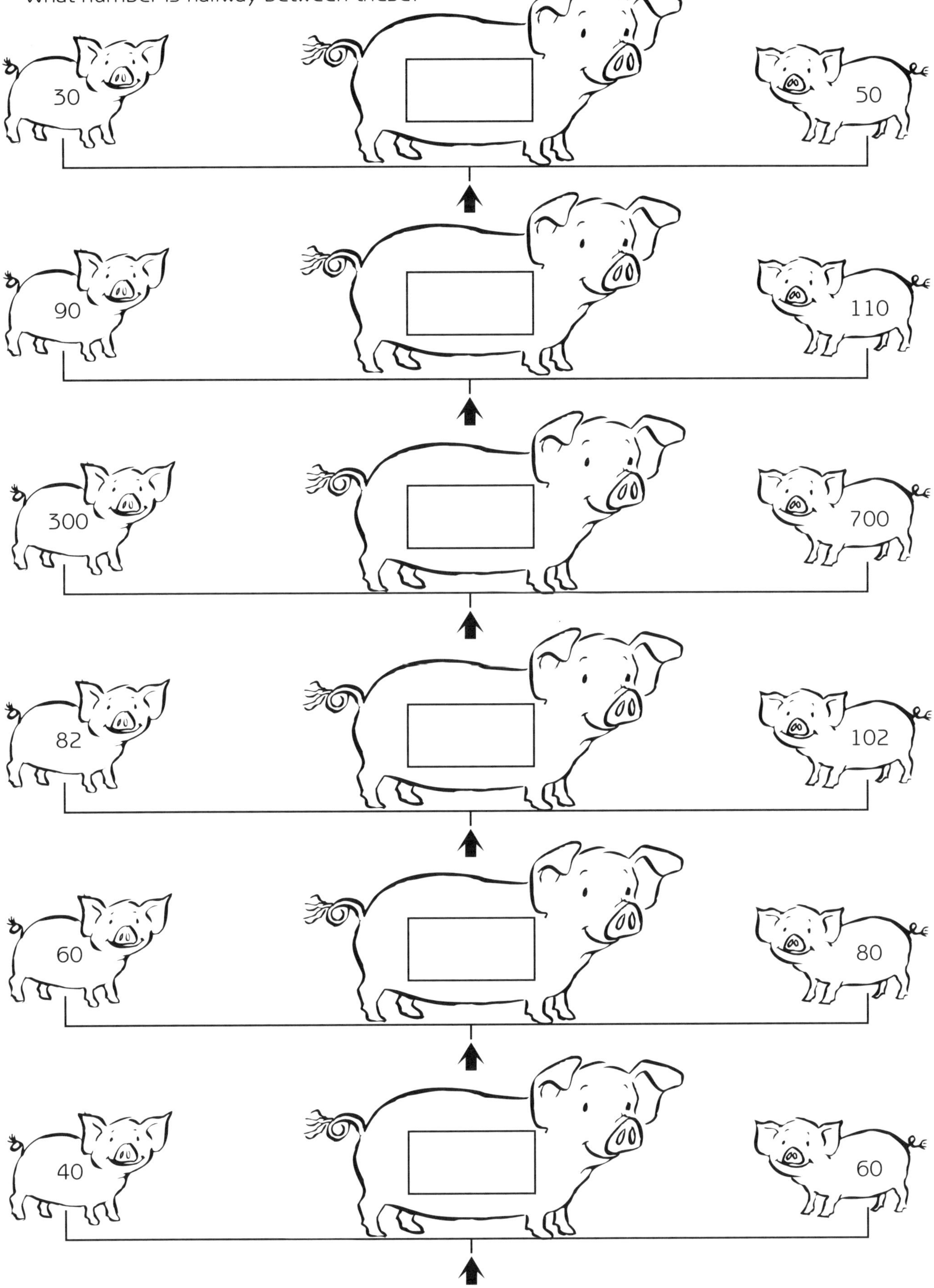

30 | | 50

90 | | 110

300 | | 700

82 | | 102

60 | | 80

40 | | 60

One hundred more or less

900 →100 more is→ ☐

231 → ☐

164 → ☐

546 → ☐

300 → ☐

298 → ☐

1000 → ☐

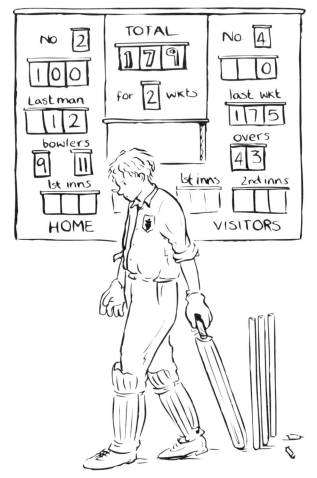

800 →100 less is→ ☐

210 → ☐

100 → ☐

532 → ☐

106 → ☐

415 → ☐

1000 → ☐

More or less: problems

Emma has 45p. Sam has 10p less than Emma.

How much does Sam have?

Ravi scores 9 runs at cricket. Ollie scores 100 more than Ravi.

How many runs did Ollie score?

Rose cycles 975 metres to school. Brian cycles 100 metres less than Rose.

How far does Brian cycle?

Julian buys 17kg of potatoes. Amma buys 1kg less than Julian.

How many potatoes does Amma buy?

Farmer Jones keeps 286 sheep on his farm. Farmer Williams keeps 100 more than Farmer Jones.

How many sheep does Farmer Williams keep?

Name _____

Keeping order

● Put these in order – smallest first.

5kg   26kg   2kg   63kg   11kg

323km   451km   167km   28km   204km

Glasgow 35m
Stirling 46m

£7.43   £8.51   £1.50   £2.45   £5.62

45cm   31cm   86cm   2cm   91cm

157   568   432   201   742

● Fill in the missing numbers.

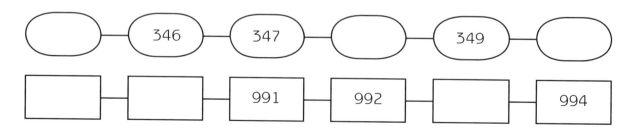

| | 346 | 347 | | 349 | |

| | | 991 | 992 | | 994 |

NO FUSS
PHOTOCOPIABLE

SCHOLASTIC
www.scholastic.co.uk

To the nearest 10

Round these numbers to the nearest 10. You could use the number lines and arrows to help you. When a number is halfway, we round up. For example, 35 rounded up to the nearest 10 is 40.

67 to the nearest 10 is _____

83 to the nearest 10 is _____

95 to the nearest 10 is _____

18 to the nearest 10 is _____

31 to the nearest 10 is _____

76 to the nearest 10 is _____

45 to the nearest 10 is _____

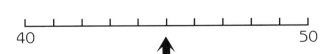

54 to the nearest 10 is _____

Name _____

To the nearest 100

Round these numbers to the nearest 100. Remember to round up any numbers that are halfway between one 100 and another. For example, 150 rounded to the nearest 100 is 200.

232 to the nearest 100 is _____

387 to the nearest 100 is _____

889 to the nearest 100 is _____

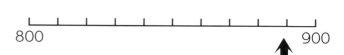

250 to the nearest 100 is _____

566 to the nearest 100 is _____

750 to the nearest 100 is _____

420 to the nearest 100 is _____

990 to the nearest 100 is _____

SCHOLASTIC
www.scholastic.co.uk

Shady fractions

● Shade $\frac{1}{2}$ of this chocolate bar.

● Shade $\frac{1}{10}$ of this chocolate bar.

● Shade $\frac{1}{10}$ of this cake.

● Shade $\frac{1}{2}$ of this cake.

 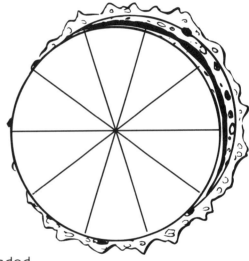

● Finish the shading until $\frac{1}{2}$ of the pattern is shaded.

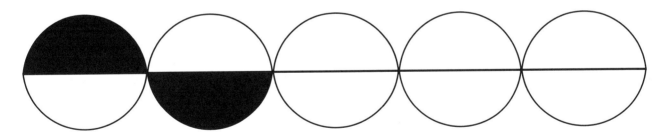

● Shade $\frac{1}{10}$ of this pattern.

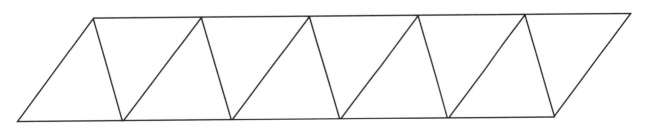

NO FUSS
PHOTOCOPIABLE

Name _____

Working out fractions

```
├──┼──┼──┼──┼──┼──┼──┼──┼──┼──┼──┼──┼──┼──┼──┼──┼──┼──┼──┼──┤
0  1  2  3  4  5  6  7  8  9  10 11 12 13 14 15 16 17 18 19 20
```

● On the number line above, what number is $\frac{1}{2}$ way?　　　　_____

● What number is $\frac{1}{4}$ of the way?　　　　_____

● What number is $\frac{3}{4}$ of the way?　　　　_____

● What number is $\frac{1}{10}$ of the way?　　　　_____

● What number is halfway between 8 and 9?　　　　_____

● What is halfway between 16 and 17?　　　　_____

● What is halfway between $1\frac{1}{2}$ and 2?　　　　_____

● What is halfway between $9\frac{1}{2}$ and 10?　　　　_____

● Estimate the fraction…

of jam in the jar　　　　of cake eaten　　　　of chocolates left

　　　　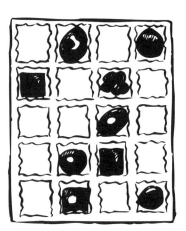

_____　　　　_____　　　　_____

SCHOLASTIC
www.scholastic.co.uk

Sum totals

● Use a number line to find two numbers that add up to 100.

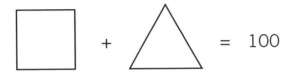

$\square$ + △ = 100

● Can you find five more pairs?

$\square$ + △ = 100

$\square$ + △ = 100

$\square$ + △ = 100

$\square$ + △ = 100

$\square$ + △ = 100

● Choose three of these numbers. Add them. _____

 104   16   69   43   97

● How many different answers can you get, choosing three numbers each time?

Name _____

Meaty sums

● Write a shopping bill of any three items.

_____

_____

_____

How much did you spend? ☐

● Choose three different items that will cost **less** in total.

_____ _____ _____

● Choose three different items that will cost **more** in total.

_____ _____ _____

Double trouble

$1 + 1 =$ ☐

$20 + 20 =$ ☐

● Use the facts above to help you find these doubles.

$19 + 19 =$ ☐ $17 + 17 =$ ☐

$18 + 18 =$ ☐ $16 + 16 =$ ☐

● Work out the answers to these in your head.

$85 + 85 =$ ☐

$65 + 65 =$ ☐

$80 + 80 =$ ☐

$70 + 70 =$ ☐

$75 + 75 =$ ☐

● Can you explain how you did it?

I want two of everything.

Name _____

Hundreds that make a thousand

● Fill in the blanks and make 1000.

500 + 500 = ☐

200 + ☐ = 1000

☐ + 600 = 1000

300 + ☐ = 1000

100 + 900 = ☐

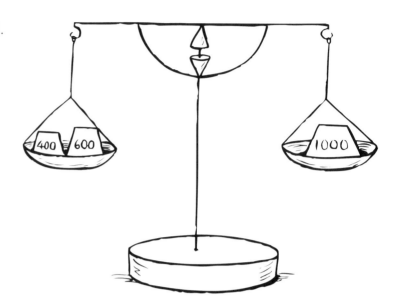

● Mr Khan travels 1000 miles in two days. On the first day he travels 600 miles. How many miles does he travel on the second day?

_____

● Mrs Jones wants to buy a car. It costs £1000. She has £800. How much more money does she need?

_____

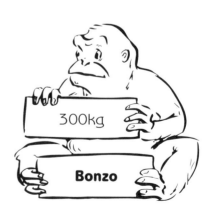

● Bozo weighs 700kg. Bonzo weighs 300kg. How much do they weigh altogether?

_____

NO FUSS PHOTOCOPIABLE

Name _____

Add it up! Write it down!

Add up these numbers. Write down your working out, as shown in the example.

56 + 32 =   (50 + 30) + (6 + 2) = 80 + 8 = 88

47 + 51 =   (   ) + (   ) =

63 + 26 =   (   ) + (   ) =

28 + 71 =   (   ) + (   ) =

65 + 34 =   (   ) + (   ) =

I'm a good adder.

68 + 27 =

36 + 45 =

77 + 19 =

62 + 57 =

85 + 64 =

Zigzags

$95 - 68 =$ | 27

Start at **68**   Add

$68 \rightarrow$ **2**

70 $\leftarrow$

$\rightarrow$ **20**

90 $\leftarrow$

$\rightarrow$ **5**

Got there! **95** $\leftarrow$
_____

27

$81 - 57 =$

Start at   Add

$58 - 29 =$

Start at   Add

$74 - 36 =$

Start at   Add

$85 - 56 =$

Start at   Add

$62 - 45 =$

Start at   Add

Multiplying problems

● Choco Cheryl ate a whole box of chocolates. There were 4 rows of 6. How many chocolates did she eat?

_____

● CD Sid collects CDs. He has 5 shelves with 10 on each shelf. How many CDs does he have altogether?

_____

● Mick the milkman delivers 3 bottles to every house in Sago Street. There are 7 houses in the street. How many bottles does he deliver?

_____

● Sara Stalk has 3 times as many roses as Rose Red. Rose has 8 roses. How many does Sara have?

_____

Name _____

Leftovers

● 18 small cakes are shared between 5 people. How many are left over?

 ● A roll of ribbon 92cm long is cut into 10cm strips. How many strips are cut? How much is left?

● What is the remainder when 17 is divided by 3?

| 35 ÷ 10 = 3 remainder 5 |

● Work out:

67 ÷ 10 =

42 ÷ 10 =

99 ÷ 10 =

● Each taxi can carry 4 passengers. How many taxis would be needed for 22 passengers?

SCHOLASTIC
www.scholastic.co.uk

Name _____

Puzzle page

● What does ★ stand for in these calculations?

9 ★ 7 = 16 _____

35 ★ 5 = 7 _____

43 ★ 78 = 121 _____

170 ★ 32 = 138 _____

16 ★ 10 = 160 _____

● Find a pair of numbers with:

a sum of 4 and a product of 4 _____

a sum of 9 and a product of 18 _____

a sum of 16 and a product of 60 _____

a sum of 7 and a product of 12 _____

a sum of 20 and a product of 100 _____

● Place all of the numbers 1, 2, 3, 4, 5 and 6 to make each side of this triangle total 9.

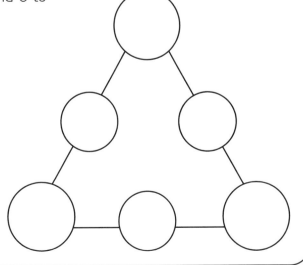

Name _____

Taking readings

Write down the measures shown.

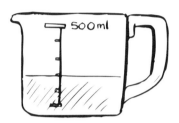

_____   _____

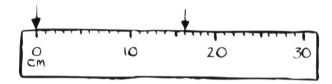

_____   _____

_____   _____

_____   _____

SCHOLASTIC
www.scholastic.co.uk

Shaping up

Connect each shape to its correct description.

Has four equal sides and four right angles

A triangle without a right angle

Has five equal sides and angles

Half a circle

A triangle with a right angle

Has four right angles. Not all the sides are the same length, but opposite sides are equal.

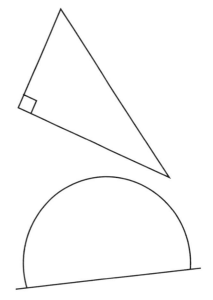

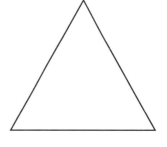

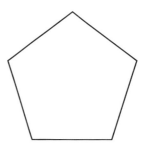

Name _____

Lines of symmetry

● Draw the lines of symmetry on these shapes.

● Do any have more than one? Do any have none at all?

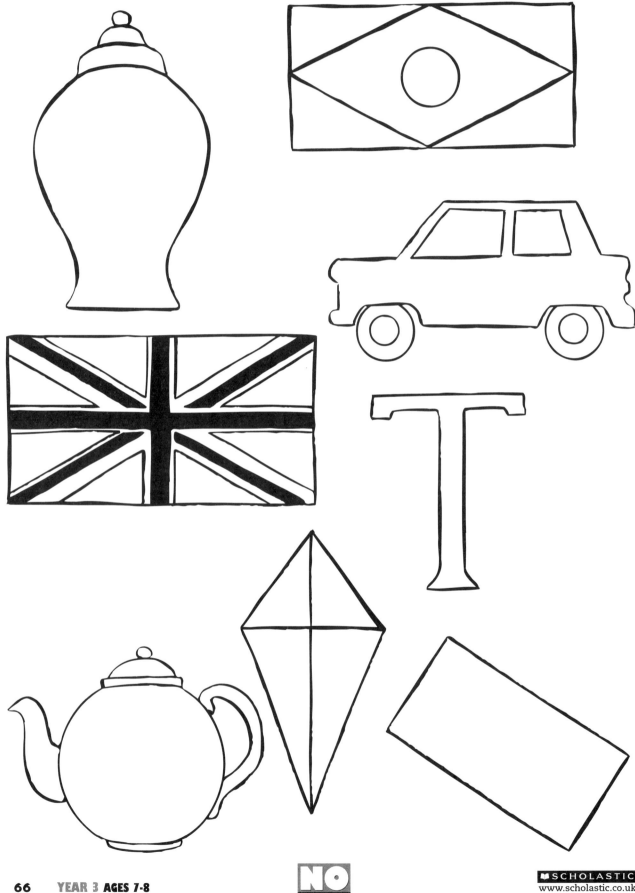

Name _____

Where are they?

The shaded square is | C2 |

Where is...?

the aeroplane | |

the bear | |

the hammer | |

the pair of spectacles | |

the fork | |

the fish | |

the flower | |

Name _____

Right angle test

Tear a strip from the bottom of this sheet. Fold it in half, then half again to make a right angle tester. Use it to say which of these angles is **more** or **less** than a right angle. Are any of them right angles?

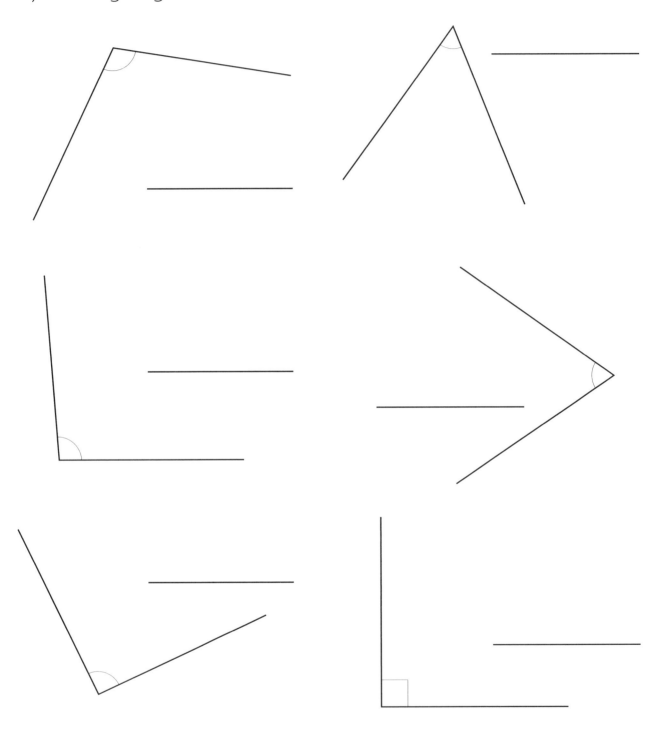

NO FUSS PHOTOCOPIABLE

Name _____

A varied diet

We eat food so that we can grow, keep healthy and be active.

Best foods for growth

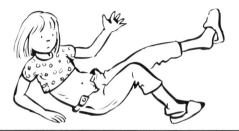

Best foods for activity

protein	**carbohydrates and fats**
milk, fish, meat, eggs, cheese, beans, nuts, peas	bread, potatoes, noodles, cereal, rice, sugar, pasta, butter, margarine, oil

For growth

For activity

Cut out these foods and put them in the correct set above.

Name _____

The truth about teeth

We have three different types of teeth.

1.	**incisors**	These have flat sides and sharp edges. Top and bottom incisors meet to cut food.
2.	**canines**	These are sharp and pointed for gripping and tearing food such as meat.
3.	**molars and premolars**	These have peaks or cusps that fit into hollows in the teeth opposite. They are for grinding and chewing food.

● Which is which?

   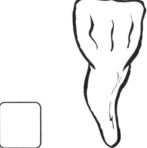   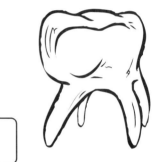

● Get your teeth into this puzzle.

Across
1. Your first teeth. Do cows make them?
3. When teeth are bad, they _____.
5. For chewing.
6. Where teeth are fixed.

Down
2. For cutting.
4. For tearing.

■SCHOLASTIC
www.scholastic.co.uk

Tooth decay

The **enamel** that covers your teeth is very tough, but if you eat a lot of sugar, **bacteria** in your mouth feed on the sugar and produce **acid** which attacks the enamel.

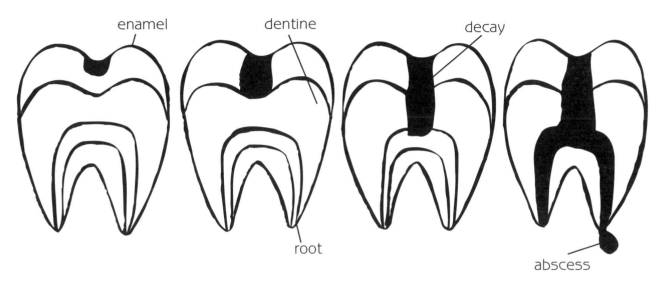

Explain what is happening here. Suggest reasons why.

Name _____

Tooth damage

less damaging

damaging

● Link these foods to their right sets.

● Can you add any more? Draw them in the sets.

■SCHOLASTIC
www.scholastic.co.uk

Name _____

Celery science

● Do this experiment. Look carefully at the head of the celery.

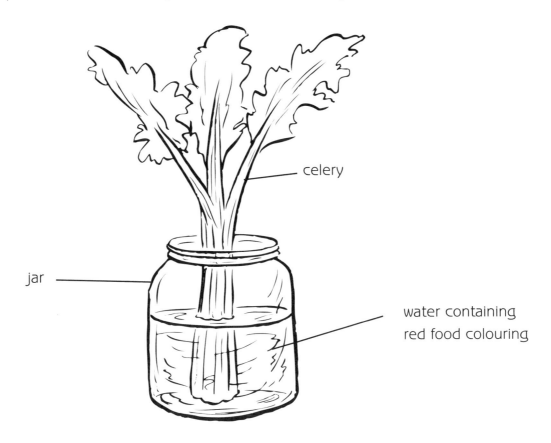

celery

jar

water containing
red food colouring

● Draw diagrams of what happens when you put the celery in the water.

1.	2.	3.

The water is _____ through the _____

to the other parts of the _____ .

Name _____

Eating the countryside

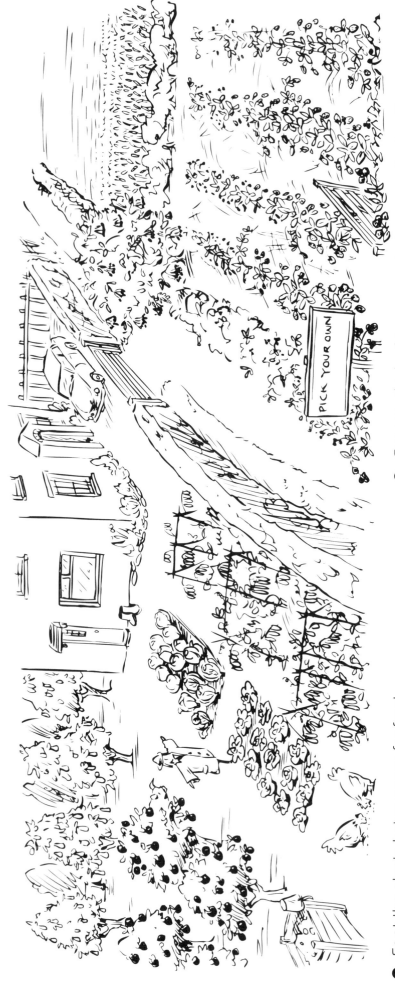

● Can you think of ten more plants we use for food?

● Spot the plants being grown for food.

Something made from...

● List all the objects you can find in the classroom made from these materials.

wood

metal

plastic

glass

● How can you tell what they are made from?

NO FUSS
PHOTOCOPIABLE

Name _____

Material match

Choose words from the list at the bottom of the page to describe these objects.

_____

_____

_____

_____

_____

_____

_____

_____

_____

_____

_____

_____

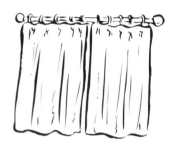

_____

_____

_____

_____

_____

_____

_____

_____

_____

_____

_____

_____

Properties of materials

hard   strong   shiny   cold

soft   flexible   smooth   dull   transparent

rough   sharp   opaque

thin   rigid   thick   stretchy   absorbent

■SCHOLASTIC
www.scholastic.co.uk

Where are the rocks?

- Mark where the rocks are in these pictures.
- Why can't we see rocks in some of the pictures? Where are they?

Name _____

Natural attraction

Find out which of these objects are attracted to a magnet.

(pencil)   (paperclip)   (drink can)   (coin)   (stick of chalk)   (scissors)   (key)

(ruler)   (pins)   (eraser)   (glass jar)   (small stone)   (nail)   (spoon)

Prediction (what I think will happen)

attracted	not attracted

Test (what actually happens)

attracted	not attracted

NO FUSS
PHOTOCOPIABLE

Name _____

Springs

● Mark or write down where the springs are in these items.

● Can you think of any other uses for springs?

Name _____

Which way?

Draw an arrow to show which direction the baby cart will move in.

Baby is pushed.

Baby is pulled.

Baby pushes against
the wall.

Baby is pulled.

www.scholastic.co.uk

OTT

● Are these objects **opaque**, **translucent** or **transparent**?

empty milk bottle

tree

mirror

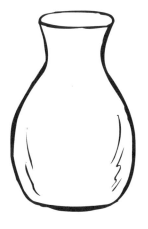

frosted glass vase

window

television

● Can you find another object for each category?

opaque	**translucent**	**transparent**

NO FUSS
PHOTOCOPIABLE

Name _____

Shapely shadows

Our bodies will not let light through them. (Things that absorb or reflect light are **opaque**.) Your shadow is the bit of ground that does not get any sunlight because your body is in the way.

Short shadows and long shadows

● Try this experiment when the Sun is shining brightly.

Stand in the same place once every hour. Ask a friend to note the position and length of your shadow each time.

● What happens to your shadow? Can you explain why?

www.scholastic.co.uk

Name _____

The sundial

Over 4000 years ago, the Babylonians invented the first shadow clock, or sundial, which they used to tell the time. A gnomon – an upright piece of metal – cast a shadow on the stone surface.

● Make your own sundial.

1. Choose a sunny spot. Turn a flowerpot upside down.

2. Put a long stick through the hole in the base of the pot and push it into the ground to make it straight and firm.

3. Every hour, use a marker pen to mark the position of the shadow cast by the stick.

You now have a sundial and can use it to tell the time.

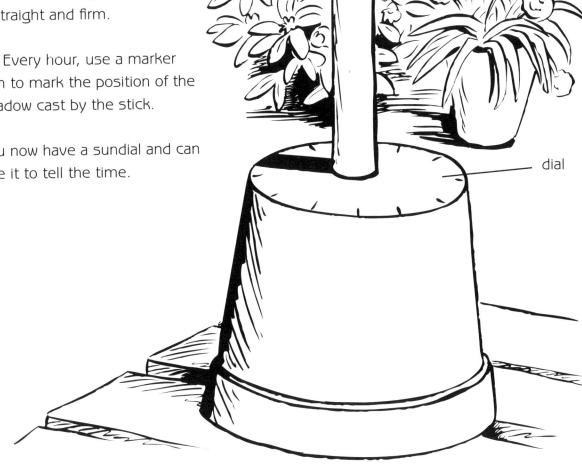

gnomon

dial

● When is your sundial no use?

Name _____

A Roman legionary

Read the passage and choose words to use in the labels.

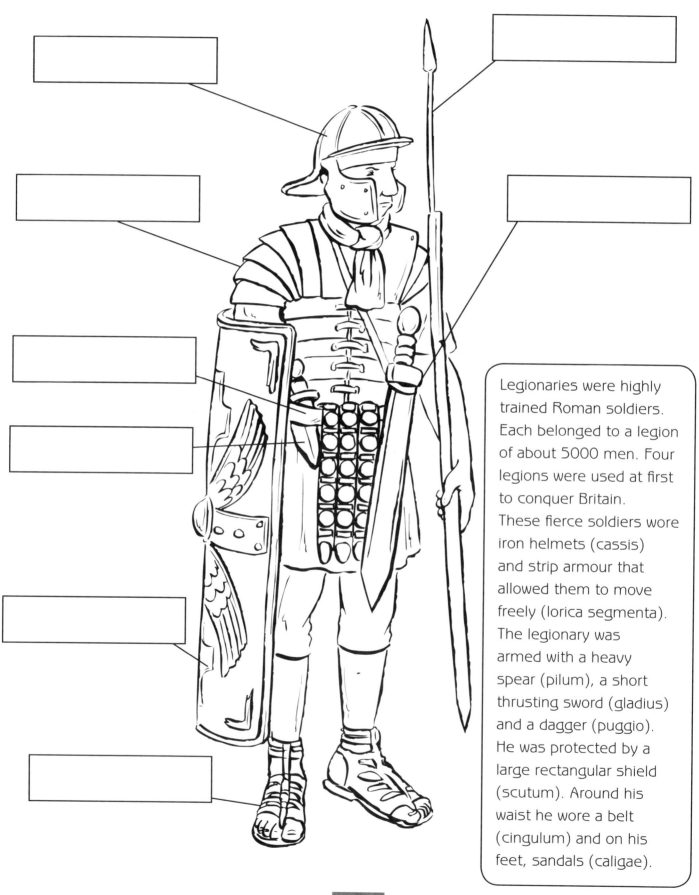

Legionaries were highly trained Roman soldiers. Each belonged to a legion of about 5000 men. Four legions were used at first to conquer Britain. These fierce soldiers wore iron helmets (cassis) and strip armour that allowed them to move freely (lorica segmenta). The legionary was armed with a heavy spear (pilum), a short thrusting sword (gladius) and a dagger (puggio). He was protected by a large rectangular shield (scutum). Around his waist he wore a belt (cingulum) and on his feet, sandals (caligae).

SCHOLASTIC
www.scholastic.co.uk

Roman mosaics

Mosaic floors were laid in public buildings and in the homes of wealthy people. The craftsman (mosaicist) made the floor pattern with cubes of coloured stone and tile called **tesserae**. This design is a **guilloche** chain.

Colour in the mosaic after looking carefully at evidence and patterns in Roman mosaics.

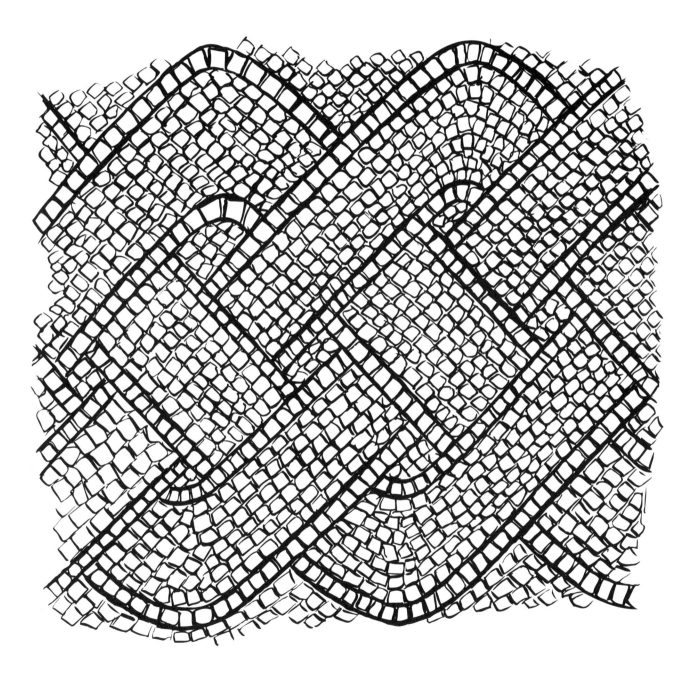

Roman mosaics are still being discovered. They have been buried under the soil for over 1000 years.

CHAPTER 4

Name _____

Public baths

Everyone enjoyed a trip to the public baths. Rome had about 1000 at one time! The baths started out as places to wash, but eventually became more like modern health clubs, with snack bars and sports facilities, and these were quite common across the Roman Empire.

This letter was written nearly 2000 years ago.

I live right over a public bath. Imagine the voices that irritate my ears. I can hear the groans of the musclemen as they swing their lead weights. They gasp and hiss. I also have to put up with the noisy slapping and pummelling of someone having a massage. Sometimes I will hear a ball-player loudly shouting out the score, or an angry drunk bellowing. Another man keeps singing in his bath and there are always people diving into the water with a splash. The hair plucker never stops shrieking, but his customers shriek even louder when he plucks their armpits. I am worn out by listening to people selling drinks, sausages and pastries. I am definitely finished.

Imagine you were selling this flat. Write the estate agent's details.

It's a riddle

The Saxons were great storytellers and they also loved riddles. Try to solve these.

> A man clad me in protective boards, covered me with hide and decked me with gold. The smith decorated me. I am an advantage to all people. What am I?

> I am wounded by weapon of iron, scarred by sword, weary from action, exhausted from the edges of the blade. Often I see battle and fight the foe.

> My father and mother abandoned me. Then a kindly wife covered me with clothes, kept me and cherished me as her own child.

> An amazing thing happened at sea. The water turned to bone!

Saxon dress

There were changes in dress in Saxon times, just as there are fashion changes today. We have evidence that some Saxon men and women would have looked something like this. Show what these labels refer to. Then colour the clothes. Saxons had yellow, red, blue and green and mixed them to make other colours like purple.

haet – a kind of round cap worn by men

braccas – close-fitting trousers

mentel – outer cloak

belt fastened by a buckle

knife fastened to the belt

leather shoes

amber or glass beads

wrist clasp to fasten cuffs

cyrtel – a gown fastened by shoulder brooches

NO FUSS

PHOTOCOPIABLE

■ SCHOLASTIC
www.scholastic.co.uk

Name _____

A Viking longboat

Number the labels according to the diagram.

A longboat had pairs of holes for **oars**. ◯

Shields were hung on the **gunwhale**. ◯

The side planks – **strakes** – overlapped. ◯

Each oarsman sat in a **room**. ◯

The vessel was built on a heavy oak **keel**. ◯

Longboats could be steered using a **steerboard** on the right-hand side at the stern. ◯

The strakes were fixed using **iron nails**. Joins were filled with tar to keep out the water. ◯

Gokstad longboat
A longboat found in Gokstad, Norway was 23 metres long. It had been buried with a man, along with 6 dogs, 12 horses and a peacock.

NO FUSS PHOTOCOPIABLE

Name _____

Where Vikings settled

Some Viking names for the places where they settled are still used today. Look at these Viking word-endings. Do you know any places to include in these lists? Use a map to find some more.

-by (farm or village)
Derby

-thorpe (small village)
Scunthorpe

-thwaite (clearing or paddock)
Braithwaite

-toft (piece of ground, farm)
Lowestoft

NO
FUSS
PHOTOCOPIABLE

■SCHOLASTIC
www.scholastic.co.uk

A kenning shield

The Vikings liked to tell stories and play with words. They were very fond of kennings, for example:

> ground ship   (**horse**)
> house stealer   (**fire**)

Look at these Viking objects and make up kennings for them. Write them in the rim of the shield.

Name _____

Job sort

Put these jobs into the groups below.

secretary	doctor	car production worker
bank manager	teacher	garage mechanic
taxi driver	salesperson	checkout operator
bank clerk	receptionist	nurse
shelf stacker	refuse collector	farmer
bricklayer	bus driver	

shop	services	transport

factory	office	other

Name _____

Climate

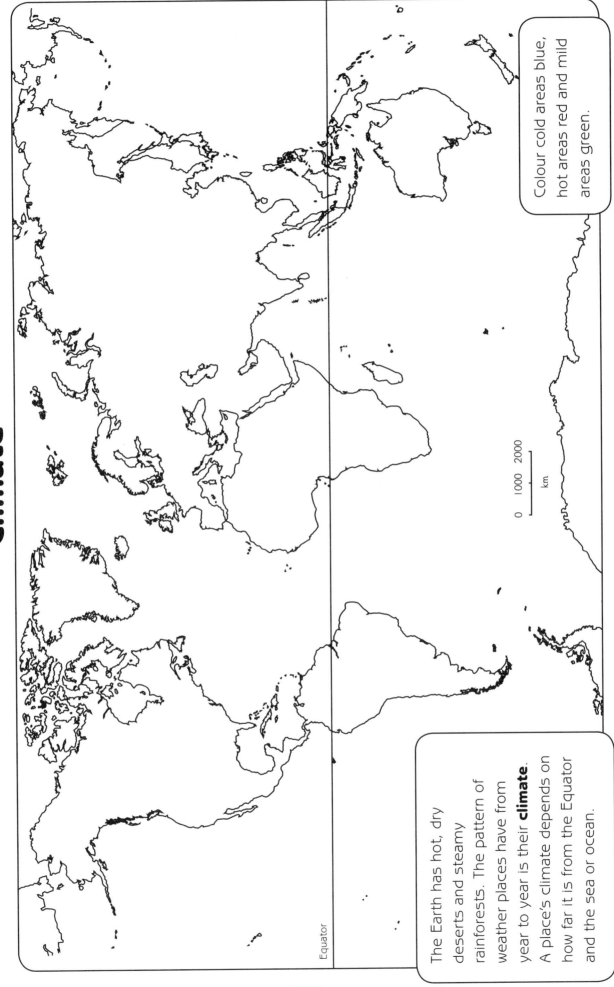

Colour cold areas blue, hot areas red and mild areas green.

Equator

0 1000 2000
km

The Earth has hot, dry deserts and steamy rainforests. The pattern of weather places have from year to year is their **climate**. A place's climate depends on how far it is from the Equator and the sea or ocean.

Name _____

Happy holidays (1)

It's nice in Nice

- Find this place in your atlas. What country is it in? _____

- What transport would you use to get here? _____

_____

- Plan your route on a map of the world.

- Make a list of what you would pack for a holiday here. _____

_____

_____

- Write a postcard to a friend saying what you have been doing at this holiday destination and what the weather is like.

Happy holidays (2)

© PHOTODISC

● Find this place in your atlas. What country is it in? _____

● What transport would you use to get here? _____

_____

● Plan your route on a map of the world.

● Make a list of what you would pack for a holiday here. _____

_____

_____

● Write a postcard to a friend saying what you have been doing at this holiday destination and what the weather is like.

Name _____

Where did it happen?

1. **Asylum seeker sought**
Police were at a loss last night as whereabouts of 20 asylum seekers made an escape from a centre to Dover. How the escape given that it was Friday but new

2. Top DJ stops spinning
but the time has come to stop for 25 years. So tomorrow will turn up at the in central London

3. **Property of the week**
Nettlefield Farm near Doncaster is very reasonable price of £1m

4. Cliffhanger in Dorset
After the heavy rains of winter declared unsafe. What will happen to properties in the area east of the Lyme Regis itself should unnecessary panic crabs and by boat but council efforts

5. Pay as you worship?
It is becoming the fashion for the cathedrals of the land to charge fees for everyone who wants to go Gloucester Cathedral has so far the temptation to change

● List the places in the news.

1. _____   4. _____

2. _____   5. _____

3. _____

● Find them on a map.

NO FUSS
PHOTOCOPIABLE

Name _____

Packaging for a purpose

● Think about a cereal packet.

● What does it protect?
● What does it contain?
● What material is it made from?
● How is it stiffened?
● What information does it show?

Name _____

Nets (1)

● This is the net of a three-dimensional (3-D) shape. If you cut it out and fold it, what 3-D shape will be made?

● Stick the net onto card. Score the dotted lines. Cut and fold to make the shape.

● Can you draw a different net for the same 3-D shape?

score and fold here

Nets (2)

What might the nets of these packages look like? Sketch your ideas.

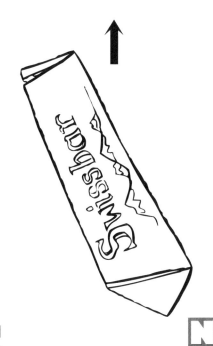

Name _____

Design and make

A sweet factory needs a package for its new chocolates. It is your job to design and make it.

Think!

Design

● What does the package need to do?

_____

_____

_____

_____

_____

● Draw your idea.

● Make it.

Checklist

What is it made from?	
Is it stiff enough?	
Does it need strengthening?	
How could it be improved?	
Does it do everything you wanted it to?	

NO FUSS
PHOTOCOPIABLE

SCHOLASTIC
www.scholastic.co.uk

Name _____

Sandwich selection

● Find out about these different sandwiches.

Name	Description	Illustration
open sandwich		
double-decker sandwich		
toasted sandwich		
filled pitta		
club sandwich		

● What sandwich would you make for Sara to eat on a cold winter's day? What ingredients would you use?

Name _____

Pneumatic gnome

● Try this!

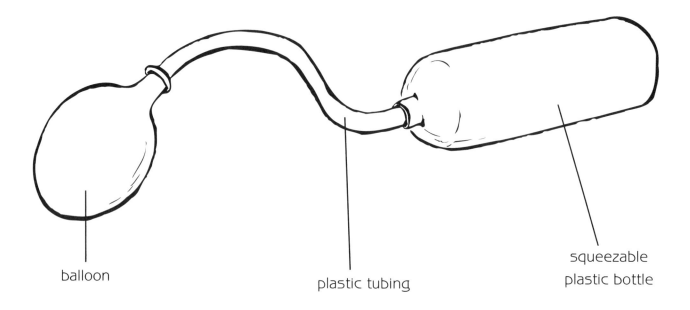

balloon   plastic tubing   squeezable
                                                             plastic bottle

● Squeeze the bottle. What happens? _____

● Use what you have discovered to make a gnome pop out of a flowerpot.

Fitting fonts

● On a computer, you can choose a font that is the size, shape and colour to fit the job it has to do. These fonts have not been used in the best way. Choose the font numbers that would match the meanings of these words.

Word	Font number

1. blocky

2. thin

3. office

4. skeleton

5. rounded

6. old

7. squashed

8. fancy

9. falling

10. happy

● Use the computer to try out the words with different fonts, weights and colours.

Business card mix-up

● Examine these business cards. Look at the font, frames, size of letters and illustrations. What is wrong? Note down how you would improve them.

John Coffin & daughter
Undertakers
5 The Mount
Heckmondwike
Tel 22541
We offer a comforting service

H. PLUG
Plumber
'service on tap'
14 Hall Green
Chorley

Tel 4312

_____ _____

_____ _____

_____ _____

_____ _____

Gardener's Place
A tool for every job
Land's Edge, Weston
Tel 9391

Jane Ward
Vicar of Dudley
welcomes you to her cheerful church
Weddings – a speciality

_____ _____

_____ _____

_____ _____

● On the computer, design your own card for a local business.

NO FUSS
PHOTOCOPIABLE

Name _____

Book cover

● Cut out the text and pictures below and arrange them to make a book cover.

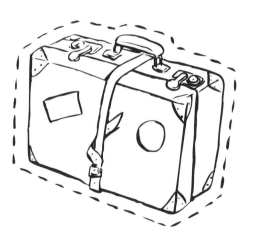

FLIGHT TO EGYPT

● Use a computer to design a cover for your favourite book.

Name _____

Computer glossary

● Match the terms to their definitions.

font

> messages sent from one person to another using a computer and telephone line

highlight

> digital art that can be placed in documents

align left/right

> place text or pictures in the middle of a page

centre

> style of type, for example Futura, Times, Helvetica

frame

> start the beginning of each object or line of text against an unseen vertical line on the left or finishing against one on the right

graphics

> select and shade text or pictures to make them stand out

e-mail

> enclose text or pictures within lines or patterns

● Design and print this information as a glossary. Add suitable pictures.

More than one (1)

● Think about this picture. Do these people know each other? How can you tell? What is the relationship between them? Why do you think the picture was painted?

● Describe:

● the people

● the pose

● the background.

© COREL

The American Farmer by Thomas Waterman Wood

Name _____

More than one (2)

● Think about this picture.

Describe:

- the people
- their characters
- their relationship
- the pose
- the background.

© COREL

Mother and son, Han Chinese

● Try for yourself. Draw or paint a large portrait of two people, one of whom is yourself. How will they pose? How will they be linked together?

NO FUSS
PHOTOCOPIABLE

■SCHOLASTIC
www.scholastic.co.uk

Patterns

● Cut out lots of copies of a shape like this one, or draw your own.

● Arrange the shape in different patterns on the grid. Rotate, reflect, transform (half drop, full drop) the shape.

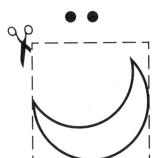

What difference does it make?

1.

2.

3.

For each sculpture:
- think about why it has been put in that place
- consider if it makes a difference to the place
- think of a few words to describe it.

_____

 1.

_____

2.

_____

3.

The frog and the snake (1)

Make musical pictures to go with this story. Write and illustrate your own ending.

The frog leaped high and far towards the babbling stream.

In the stream, the water snake swam smoothly. Slowly it slithered to the shore.

When the snake saw the frog, it froze. It waited and waited, not moving a muscle.

Name _____

The frog and the snake (2)

Cheerfully unaware of the danger, the frog bounced nearer and nearer.

Hidden at the edge of the babbling brook, the snake waited for its meal. Then…

_____

_____

_____

NO FUSS
PHOTOCOPIABLE

Ostinati

A repeated pattern of music is called an **ostinato**.
These rhythm patterns fit the words beneath them.

    is a silent beat.

● Clap each ostinato six times. Hear the silent beat 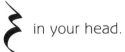 in your head.

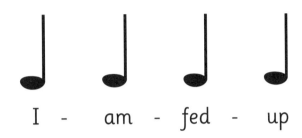

I - am - fed - up

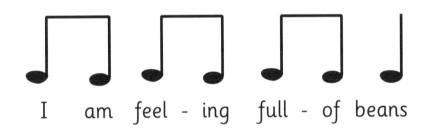

I   am   feel - ing   full - of   beans

wib - ble   wob - ble   wib - ble   wob - ble

pease   pud-ding   hot

● Make up an ostinato of your own.

Name _____

Signs and symbols

A **sign** has one clear meaning. A **symbol** can have many meanings that may not be clear and may mean different things to different people. Sort these into signs and symbols. Then write down what you think they mean.

Name _____

Objects and memories

Objects can remind us of special occasions or good moments. Choose one of these pictures and write about the memories it brings back.

1.

2.

3.

4.

Picture [   ] reminds me of _____

_____

_____

_____

_____

Name _____

Passover

Food can remind us of special events. During the eight days of Passover, Jewish families eat nothing that contains yeast. This is to remind them that when the Jewish people escaped from slavery in Egypt (about 3300 years ago), there was no time to wait for bread to rise. On the eve of Passover, Jews eat a Seder meal. Each of the foods in the meal is a symbol of the escape.

If you were making a meal to remind you of home, what food would it contain?

_____

_____

_____

_____

_____

The Passover meal

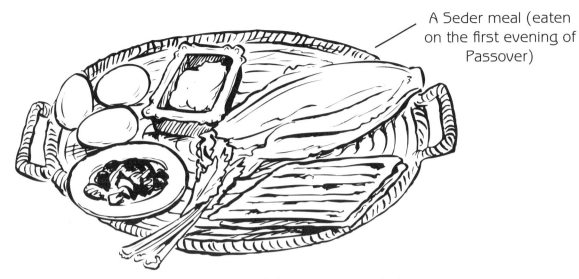

A Seder meal (eaten on the first evening of Passover)

Draw a line to match the food with the part of the story it symbolises.

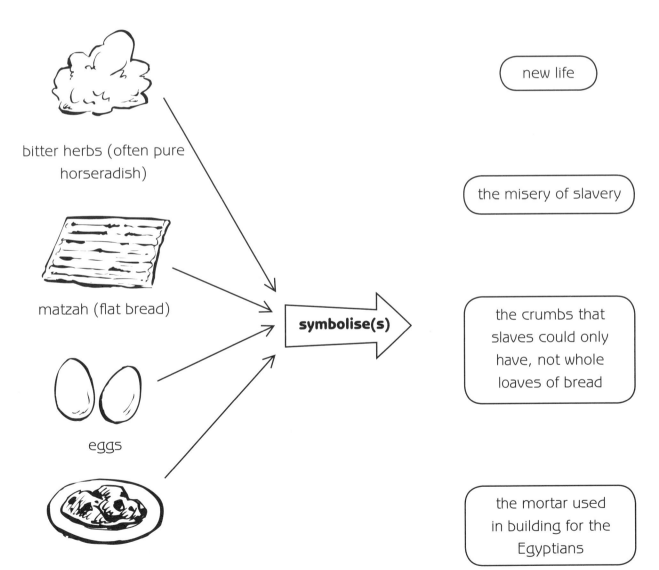

bitter herbs (often pure horseradish)

matzah (flat bread)

eggs

charoset (a paste of fruit and nuts mixed with wine)

symbolise(s)

new life

the misery of slavery

the crumbs that slaves could only have, not whole loaves of bread

the mortar used in building for the Egyptians

Name _____

More than they say

Religious language is special. It is used to describe many things that are important and can be difficult to explain. Here are some metaphors from the Bible. Can you explain what they mean?

The truth will be your shield.

The Lord is my shepherd.

Jesus is the light of the world.

www.scholastic.co.uk

Diwali cards

Diwali is the Hindu festival of lights. Many Hindus send cards to wish people a happy Diwali. The cards often picture the gods important in the Diwali story.

● Design and make a Diwali card of your own. You could use one or more of these pictures on it.

● Find out more about Diwali.

Name _____

Find out about the Bible

● Complete this passage using the words at the bottom of the page.

The Bible is a very special book to _____.

It is treated with great respect, so is called the

_____ Bible. The Bible is divided into two main

sections called Testaments. The first is the _____

Testament, the second is the _____ Testament.

The second Testament begins with the birth of

_____. The Bible is one book, but it is made up of

many smaller _____. People who follow this faith

learn how to be good Christians from the Bible. They read

it at home and especially in _____.

(books) (Holy) (church) (New) (Old) (Jesus) (Christians)

● Find out two more facts about the Bible.

NO FUSS
PHOTOCOPIABLE

Saving for something special

To do or have some things, you need to save up your money.

What are the best ways to save money? Put these in order.

✂ -

A.   Keep putting it into your purse or wallet.

B.   Hide it under your bed.

C.   Give it to a friend to look after.

D.   Put it in a bank account.

E.   Put it in a savings account that earns interest.

F.   Bury spare coins in the garden.

Jobs: likes and dislikes (1)

Imagine what it is like to go to work every day. You earn money, you meet people, but you must be there when you are supposed to and you have to work hard all day. You can't take a day off just when you like. Write down what you think this person might like and dislike about his job.

Firefighter

good   bad

NO
FUSS
PHOTOCOPIABLE

SCHOLASTIC
www.scholastic.co.uk

Jobs: likes and dislikes (2)

Imagine what it is like to go to work every day. You earn money, you meet people, but you must be there when you are supposed to and you have to work hard all day. You can't take a day off just when you like. Write down what you think this person might like and dislike about her job.

CHAPTER 11

Name _____

Jobs: likes and dislikes (3)

Imagine what it is like to go to work every day. You earn money, you meet people, but you must be there when you are supposed to and you have to work hard all day. You can't take a day off just when you like. Write down what you think this person might like and dislike about her job.

Bank clerk

good

bad

 NO FUSS PHOTOCOPIABLE

Jobs: likes and dislikes (4)

Imagine what it is like to go to work every day. You earn money, you meet people, but you must be there when you are supposed to and you have to work hard all day. You can't take a day off just when you like. Write down what you think this person might like and dislike about his job.

Builder

good

bad

Beating bullying

What if this happened to you? Work with a friend to write four tips for beating bullying.

No more bullying

 1.

 2.

 3.

4.

NO FUSS
PHOTOCOPIABLE

SCHOLASTIC
www.scholastic.co.uk

Name _____

Looking after yourself

How I look after my...	
teeth	
feet	
hands	
hair	
body	

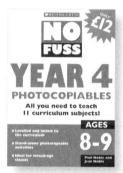

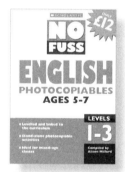
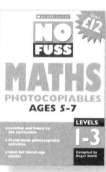
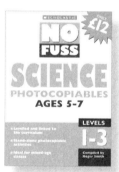
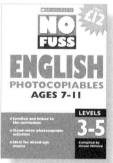
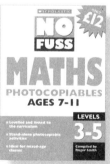
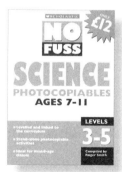